Europe without George

By <u>IRENE</u> <u>KAMPEN</u>

LIFE WITHOUT GEORGE

WE THAT ARE LEFT

THE ZIEGFELDS' GIRL
(with Patricia Ziegfeld
and Suzanne Gleaves)

Europe without George

BY IRENE KAMPEN

ILLUSTRATED BY *Whitney Darrow, Jr.*

W • W • NORTON & COMPANY • INC • NEW YORK

Europe
without
George

CHAPTER *1*

THOMAS COOK AND SONS
ITINERARY FOR MRS. IRENE KAMPEN
            MISS CHRISTINE KAMPEN
EUROPEAN TOUR—LONDON, EDINBURGH, LUCERNE,
FLORENCE, NAPLES, SORRENTO, VENICE,
ROME, ATHENS, NICE, PARIS.

"We're going to Europe!" I told Charley MacAllaster, bubbling over with girlish enthusiasm. "We're leaving July first and we'll be gone for six weeks. Isn't that wonderful?"

"Great!" Charley said. "You'll love it. Just make sure you keep away from the big, fancy hotels."

"Big fancy hotels are no good?" I asked.

"Tourist traps," Charley said. "If you're only interested in ice-water and indoor plumbing you might as well stay here in Connecticut. Right?"

"Right," I said. "Check and double-check."

"You certainly don't want to go over there acting like a typical American tourist," Charley said.

"Heaven forbid," I said.

Europe without George   **11**

"Which boat you sailing on?" Charley asked.

"We're not sailing on any boat," I said. "We're flying."

"Oh," Charley said. "Flying." There was a brief silence. "Which airline?" he asked.

I told him. There was another, and slightly more ominous, silence.

"How come?" Charley said.

"What do you mean, how come?" I said. "What's the matter with it?"

"It's a *domestic* airline," Charley said earnestly. "Domestic airlines don't understand the first thing about service. Listen, take my advice and change your tickets to TJA."

"What's TJA?" I asked him.

"Trans-Jugoslavian," Charley said. "The service aboard is fantastic. Hot towels, in-flight movies with English subtitles, and nine hours later you're in Dubrovnik."

"I don't want to be in Dubrovnik," I said.

"You don't want to be in Dubrovnik?" Charley said incredulously. "Are you serious?"

"Why would I want to be in Dubrovnik?" I said. "Dubrovnik is in Jugoslavia."

"So?" Charley said.

"Jugoslavia is a Communist country," I said.

"Oh for God's sake, that's just a lot of *Time* magazine propaganda," Charley said impatiently. "Listen, if you're not going to Dubrovnik, where the hell *are* you going?"

"London," I said. "Edinburgh, Lucerne, Florence, Naples, Sorrento, Venice, Rome, Athens, Nice, and Paris. And we're also taking a cruise of the Greek Islands."

"You're trying to cover too much territory," Charley

said. "You ought to pick out one spot and stay there for the whole six weeks. Dubrovnik, for instance."

"Charley," I said, "I do not, repeat, *n-o-t*, wish to go to Dubrovnik."

Charley shrugged.

"It's your funeral," he said. "All I can say is, anyone who goes to Europe and doesn't see Dubrovnik might just as well stay home."

"Europe!" Mrs. Caudlemaier said. "How exciting! Marvin and I went last summer. What is your itinerary?"

"London," I began. "Then a tour up through . . ."

"London?" Mrs. Caudlemaier said, recoiling. "In *July*?"

"London in July is no good?" I said.

"But my dear, it's the rainy season," Mrs. Caudlemaier said. "I wore a woolen suit and two sweaters the whole time we were there and I nearly got pneumonia. Dreadful. Take my advice—forget London."

"Forget London?" I said.

"And if you *must* go, be sure and take along plenty of plastic vegetable bags," Mrs. Caudlemaier said. "The kind with zipper tops."

"What for?" I asked.

"To pack your wet overshoes in," Mrs. Caudlemaier said.

". . . and Edinburgh and Lucerne," I told Cousin Sarah. "And then we're booked for a boat trip from Naples to Sorrento."

"When is the boat trip?" Cousin Sarah asked.

"July," I said.

"Well, all I can say is, I hope you're a good sailor," Cousin Sarah said in a discouraging voice.

"Buy a little notebook," Bellman Potterfield told me. "Like this one. Divide it into sections for every country on your itinerary and write down the things people recommend to you. That's what I did when Sam Katzenbaum and I were over there on a Fulbright last year."

Bellman disappeared into the kitchen to mix some drinks. I picked up his little notebook.

"France," I read. *"Chou-Chou DeFour, 12 Rue de Montalembert stacked (Sam Katzenbaum). Babette Liseux, doesn't speak English but hot number (Sam Katzenbaum) phone Annecy 534 . . ."*

"Be sure and take along plenty of toilet paper," Wilma Vogelsang said to me. "And ball-point pens. Europeans are mad for ball-point pens. You can use them for tips and things."

I opened my little notebook, and under *"Miscellaneous"* I wrote *"Toilet paper, ball-point pens (Wilma Vogelsang)."*

"I envy you," Wilma said. "I'm mad for Europe. Especially Paris."

"We get to Paris after our Greek cruise," I said. "Around the middle of August."

"August?" Wilma said. "You're going to Paris in August?"

"August is no good?" I said.

"But my dear, no one is *there* in August," Wilma said. "All the real Parisians are gone. The shops are boarded up.

Europe without George

The decent restaurants are shuttered. Paris is literally *closed* in August."

"Got a pencil?" the manager of the Piggly-Wiggly meat department said to me. "Okay—write this down. *Ferragambino's.*"

I opened my notebook and under *"Italy"* I wrote down *"Ferragambino's. (Manager of Piggly-Wiggly Meat Department)."*

"It's a little restaurant in Settignano," the manager said. "They serve the best fettucini in the world. This place is off the beaten track, not all crapped up with American tourists."

"We aren't going to Settignano," I said.

He stared at me.

"You aren't going to Settignano?" he said. "What's the point of going to Italy if you miss Settignano?"

"Cook's didn't put it on the itinerary," I said.

"Itinerary!" he said. "I bet they've got you booked into every tourist trap in Italy, up to and including Venice."

"Venice is no good?" I said.

"Venice!" he said scornfully. "Do you know what Venice is?"

"No," I said. "What is Venice?"

"Venice is Coney Island," the manager of the Piggly-Wiggly meat department said. "With pigeons."

"What kind of a car are you buying over there?" Evelyn asked me. "A Peugeot is very good, especially for driving through the Alps."

"We're not buying a car," I said.

"You're not buying a *car*?" Evelyn said. "You're going to travel around in buses with a lot of Americans?"

"Americans in buses are no good?" I said.

"You don't get to see any of the real country that way," Evelyn said. "You don't get to poke around in funny little out-of-the-way places."

"What's the point of poking around in funny little out-of-the-way places when I can't speak the language?" I said.

"Don't you and Chris speak any foreign languages at all?" Evelyn asked.

"Chris had four years of Latin," I said. "I speak a little French. A smattering of Greek."

"Say something in Greek," Evelyn said.

"Diochete Upsala," I said.

"What does that mean?" Evelyn asked.

" *'Through Aspiration We Shall Reach The Stars,'* " I said. "It's the motto of Chris's sorority."

"Well, I suppose it may find you a good restaurant in Athens," Evelyn said. "One final word of advice—watch out for European men. They pinch."

"Connecticut men do too," I said.

"But a pinch doesn't mean the same thing in Europe," Evelyn said. "Over there it's merely a friendly gesture. Try and keep the U.N. charter in mind."

"How come you know so much about Europe?" I asked her. "You've never been outside the United States."

"I met a fellow who was there last year on a Fulbright," Evelyn said. "He told me all about it. He's a friend of Bellman Potterfield."

"You're not by any chance speaking of good old Sam Katzenbaum?" I asked.

"Yes," Evelyn said. "Do you know him?"

"I know *of* him," I said.

I met Harry pawing through the Reduced Imported Chianti barrel (SPECIAL! THIS WEEK ONLY! FINE ITALIAN WINE 83¢ QUART!) in the Highmeadow Liquor store.

"All set for your trip?" he asked me.

"Everybody keeps telling us we're doing it all wrong," I said. "Everybody says to forget London."

"Forget London?" Harry said.

"And Paris," I said. "Everybody says we ought to go to Dubrovnik and Moscow instead."

"I understand the Viet Cong Hilton is opening up next month too," Harry said. "Rates should be fairly cheap in the summer months. Have you got the number of your flight to London yet?"

"It's flight number two," I said.

"I know the guys on that run," Harry said. "I'll have them keep an eye out in case you need any little extras in the way of service."

"You mean little extras like the foreign airlines give?" I said. "Hot towels? In-flight movies?"

"The captain and the co-pilot do ancient Kabuki dances on the flight deck," Harry said.

"Who flies the plane?" I asked him.

"The head stewardess," Harry said. "Only don't tell the FAA. We have enough trouble as it is."

Chris and I were ready at last. We had our vaccination certificates, our airline tickets, our passports ("How about fixing your hair or something, girlie," the passport photographer said to Chris), our traveler's checks, and a policy insuring our baggage against everything except war or inherent vice.

We had our drip-dry dresses, our walking shoes, our rain-or-shine coats, and our plastic vegetable bags with zippered tops. We had ball-point pens, toilet paper, nylon stockings, soap, and twenty-five rolls of Kodak Instamatic Color Film, all of which we had been assured were unobtainable in the Old World. The Kodak Instamatic Film was packed into the plastic vegetable bags with the zippered tops.

We had a letter of introduction from the Highmeadow librarian to a cousin of her mother's who lived in Lucerne. We had a currency converter that gave the value of the American dollar in francs, pounds, and lire when you turned a little plastic dial. We had a copy of *A Happy Trip in All Languages*" listing fifty common English phrases along with their translation and phonetic pronunciation ("To your health!—*à votre santé!*—av-vawtre saw'ng-TAY!" "Take me to the hotel—*Andiamo all'albergo*—ahn-DYAH-mo ahl ahl-BAIR-go!"). I carried the phrasebook and Chris carried the currency converter.

We stood in front of the bus stop on Main street waiting for the airport limousine. Our Bon Voyage party was made up of Moose Minifee, in Beethoven sweatshirt and ski goggles, Moose's little brother, and Wilma Vogelsang. Wilma hadn't come downtown especially to see us off, she told us.

Europe without George

She was waiting for her sheets to get finished in the laundromat.

Moose said he had just heard a bulletin on the radio that a tourist bus had fallen off a Swiss alp into a Swiss lake, killing everybody aboard.

"Switzerland is a beautiful country," Wilma said. "But treacherous."

Moose's little brother asked Chris to send him some stamps for his collection when she got to West Berlin.

"We're not ging to West Berlin," Chris said.

"You're not going to West Berlin?" Moose's brother said in disbelief. "You're not going to see the Berlin Wall?"

"No, and we're not going to see the crematory ovens at Belsen either," I told him. "This is a pleasure trip."

"Holy cow, I don't see why anybody bothers to go to Europe at all if they don't see the Berlin Wall," Moose's brother said.

MONDAY, JULY 1.
LEAVE NEW YORK AT 20:00 (FLIGHT 2)
FOR HEATHROW AIRPORT, LONDON.

      The seats in the Tourist Class section of the jet were three abreast. I had the window seat and Chris had the seat next to me. A good-looking boy in a madras jacket and Ivy League trousers sat down in the aisle seat.

Chris fixed her hair.

The pilot got on the loudspeaker and cheered everybody up by saying that the stewardesses would now demonstrate the correct procedure for abandoning the airplane over the Atlantic Ocean. The stewardesses lined up in the aisle and showed us how to put on the lifejackets that were stored under the seats and the oxygen masks that were stored above our heads. After that they distributed illustrated little booklets appetizingly entitled *"Emergency Survival Procedures."*

As soon as we were airborne, Chris and Madras Jacket (who turned out to be Dixon St. Clair, Choate '62, Harvard '66) tilted their seats back and plunged into conversation. I tried to tilt back too, but no matter how hard I pressed on the little button I stayed bolt upright, clutching both armrests of my chair like Cleopatra being borne into Rome.

"What's the matter with your mother?" Dixon St. Clair asked Chris. "She looks funny."

"Nothing's the matter with me," I said. "I can't get my seat to go back."

"Just press the button and scroonsh back hard against the seat," Chris said.

The first officer, resplendent in blue uniform and gold braid, appeared at our side and asked if my name was Irene Kampen.

"Why yes, it is," I said, giving him a glittering smile and scroonshing back hard against the seat.

"Captain Connors told us you'd be on this flight," the first officer said. "Allow me to welcome you aboard."

"How kind," I said, and nodded at him graciously like Queen Victoria. I gave another scroonsh and suddenly the seat tilted forward into what the Emergency Survival booklet described as *Ditching Position* ("Fasten seat belt, remove high-heeled shoes, extinguish cigarettes, and lean slightly forward, bracing the knees.")

"No need to be nervous," the first officer said. "We expect a perfectly smooth flight."

"I'm not ner—" I began, when with a loud click from the armrest the seat flew backward and I found myself reclining in the manner of Manet's *Olympia,* gazing up enigmatically into the eyes of the passenger behind me.

"Well, I guess I'll be getting back to work," the first officer said, eying me with faint alarm. I gave him another gracious smile and pressed the button once more, shooting myself forward again into the old Ditching Position.

"Dixon says we're crazy to go to Lucerne," Chris told me. "Dixon says Lucerne is full of American tourists. Dixon says we ought to go straight to Paris and stay there the whole six weeks."

"Paris is closed," I said.

"Would you like something to read?" the stewardess asked. "The *Herald-Tribune? Newsweek?* The latest issue of *Life?*"

I took the latest issue of *Life.*

". . . Luxurious liners sail out of the Athens port of Piraeus on four-to-five day cruises of the Greek islands. However, it is best to avoid the months of July and August when a hot wind, known as the *meltemi,* blows ceaselessly from the north . . ."

A Traveler's Guide To Greece
Life Magazine
Issue of July 1, 1963

CHAPTER 2

TUESDAY, JULY 2.
ARRIVE LONDON.

It was raining in London.

I looked out our hotel room window and there across the street was Hyde Park. We are really here, I said to myself. We are really here on this sceptered isle this England William the Conqueror shall stand tiptoe when summer is icumen in twelve fifteen A.D. theirs not to reason why because here lies Arthur the Once and Future King.

"I wonder if I'll get a letter from Moose while we're in London," Chris said.

"—and Hengist and Horsa too," I said.

There was a knock on the door. A bellboy dressed like Ethelred The Unready came in with our valises and began to bustle around unfolding luggage stands, testing closet doors, and fluffing out the draperies.

"I shall just check the geyser," he said, and disappeared

into the bathroom. I caught a glimpse of gleaming brass fixtures and white marble.

"I'm certainly glad Charley MacAllaster isn't around," I said. I took a handful of brand-new English money out of my purse. "Which one of these do you suppose is a shilling?"

"Do you think a shilling is enough for a tip?" Chris said. "Three valises, remember."

"The worst thing an American tourist can do is begin to overtip all over the place the minute he gets abroad," I said. "It gives foreigners the impression that we're all vulgar and money-mad."

Ethelred The Unready came out of the bathroom and I handed him his tip. He looked at it. Then he carried it over to the window and looked at it some more, his face meanwhile registering disbelief.

"Oh, God, it's probably too small," I said apprehensively to Chris.

"How about giving him one of the ball-point pens?" Chris said.

The bellboy walked back, handed me the coin, and said, with dignity, "Madame, you have given me sixpence."

"I'm terribly sorry," I said. I fumbled inside my wallet and pulled out a bill. "Here. Thank you very much."

" 'Kew," he said, and left.

"What was that you gave him?" Chris asked.

"A pound," I said. "Look it up on the currency converter."

Chris looked it up.

"Two dollars and eighty-two cents," she said.

WEDNESDAY, JULY 3.

AFTERNOON DRIVE OF CITY VIA BUCKINGHAM PALACE,
TRAFALGAR SQUARE, AND PICCADILLY.
VISIT TO LONDON MUSEUM AND TOWER OF LONDON.

A lot of Americans were milling around inside the Cook's office, cashing traveler's checks and complaining about their hotel rooms. Over in a corner underneath a sign that said LONDON TOUR a gray-haired lady with an accent so British as to be nearly unintelligible was herding a group of tourists together. We joined them, and the lady led us all out to a sightseeing bus parked at the curb.

It was raining harder than ever.

When we were all seated in the bus, cameras at the ready, the lady guide said into the microphone that we had a great deal of sightseeing to do and anyone who didn't keep up with the party would be left behind. She sounded quite stern about it.

"Very well, Alfred," she said to the driver. "*Allons!*"

Alfred gunned the motor, jammed his foot down on the accelerator, and we roared away in a cloud of exhaust fumes.

"I wonder if it's raining back in Milwaukee," the man behind us said to his wife.

"How long would it take a letter to get to London if Moose mailed it yesterday in Connecticut?" Chris asked.

With a shriek of tires Alfred rounded a corner on two wheels.

"Dead ahead you will see Buckingham Palace," the guide said into the microphone. "Unfortunately, we are just too late to witness the exciting ceremony known as the trooping of the colors."

"What was that about looping?" the man from Milwaukee said to his wife. "I can't understand a Goddam word the woman says."

"Not looping," his wife said. "Drooping. Something about drooping crullers."

We whizzed past the palace, tore around another corner, and Trafalgar Square hove into view.

The guide mumbled into the microphone.

"*Now* what the hell is she saying?" the man said.

"Lord Nelson did something here, I think," his wife told him. She pointed to the Winged Victory atop the cenotaph. "That's his statue."

"That's Lord Nelson?" her husband asked dubiously. "What's he wearing a dress for?"

"If you glance quickly to your left you will see the world-famous Houses of Parliament," the guide said.

Everybody glanced quickly to their left, straight into the window of an F. W. Woolworth store piled high with a display of Kodak Instamatic Film.

"Sorry," the guide said briskly. "I meant to say, to your right. Too late now, I fear. However, if you will glance sharply backward you will catch a glimpse of the Bank of England. Those who wish to take photographs may do so."

Everybody turned around and snapped their Kodaks and Rolleiflexes, thus obtaining many interesting shots of the backs of each other's heads. After that Alfred drove hell-for-leather to the London Museum, where we piled out of the bus and raced through the rooms at a dog-trot after the

Europe without George

guide. Then back into the bus again, and a mad ride to the Tower of London. The Tower itself was nearly obscured by rain and the Beefeaters had all donned black rubberized raincoats over their colorful uniforms, thereby rendering themselves indistinguishable from members of the New York City Police Department.

Back on the bus again the guide counted noses and announced happily that three of the party were missing.

"We won't wait," she said. "I warned them."

Alfred gunned the motor again and we sped through the London streets, homeward bound. The lights of the Houses of Parliament gleamed across the black Thames water, and the great dome of St. Paul's was silhouetted against the leaden sky. We pulled up in front of the Cook's office just as Big Ben struck six o'clock.

"It is customary for each passenger to present the driver with a small tip upon leaving the bus," the guide announced.

Alfred produced a white china saucer from somewhere and set it on the dashboard. As the passengers filed down the aisle there was a steady clink-clink of coins being tossed into the saucer.

"What are you going to leave?" Chris asked me.

"I don't know," I said. "I'll see what the others gave him."

As we neared the front of the bus I peered into the saucer. There were a few shilling pieces, an American quarter, a Canadian dime, and a coin with a hole in the center that looked like a Japanese yen. I quietly added the sixpence that Ethelred The Unready had given back to me that morning, and Chris and I climbed down from the bus.

"Where are we going to have dinner tonight?" Chris asked.

I opened the little black notebook to the section labeled *"London."*

"The Hound and Horn," I read. *"Quaint Eng pub fish and ch dartboard jolly barmaid (Mrs. Caudlemaier)."*

"Let's try this place," I said. "Mrs. Caudlemaier said it's tucked away on a little back street somewhere and that it's an authentic remnant of old Cockney London."

It took us nearly an hour to locate Mrs. Caudlemaier's quaint English pub. We finally found it at the very end of a winding, cobblestoned street not far from Kensington Gardens. Sure enough, there was a dartboard on the wall and a barmaid in mobcap and steel-rimmed spectacles polishing the top of the bar with a cloth. She asked us if we had reservations. I told her we didn't.

"Can't eat 'ere without a reservation," the jolly barmaid said, and went back to her polishing.

"There's a back table they could sit at, Myrt," one of the waiters said to her.

"Well, all right, but they'll 'ave to eat and get out in an hour," Myrt said reluctantly. "That table's reserved for Lord Warburton at eight."

The waiter led us to a back table and handed us two menus written with pale violet ink in Olde English script. The first item on the menu was Fmoked Baby Falmon £2 6d. Underneath the Fmoked Baby Falmon was Chateaubriand Bearnaife £3 5s, or nine dollars, or exactly the same price charged at that quaint old New York City pub, The Forum Of The Twelve Caesars.

"I don't see any fish and chips on this menu," Chris said.

The waiter had appeared again and was standing with his pencil at the ready, so we ordered Dover Sole (or Dover Fole), the cheapest thing on the menu. The waiter stalked away, his back eloquent with frosty disapproval.

"Why, there's Dixon St. Clair!" Chris said, as a festive group of people in evening dress came into the restaurant and perched on stools at the bar, greeting the barmaid with easy familiarity and ordering champagne cocktails all around.

"Hello there!" Dixon said, spotting us. He came over to our table. He was wearing a white dinner jacket, black trousers, and a maroon cummerbund. "Well, imagine running into you like this! I just dashed across from Paris for the weekend."

"How is Paris?" I asked him.

He said Paris was heaven.

"Divine weather," he said. "Terribly gay. How is London?"

"Wet," I said, "but terribly gay also."

"We're going to the theater tonight," Chris told him. *Beyond The Fringe.*"

"Terribly amusing show," Dixon said, "although I wish you could have seen it last season with the original company. The cast they've got in it now isn't nearly as good, I hear."

"What happened to the original company?" I asked.

"They're in New York doing it on Broadway," he said. "Well, awfully good to have seen both of you. I'll be dashing along now."

He left us with a bow.

"Doesn't he look divine?" Chris said, sighing. "I just love British men in evening clothes."

"British?" I said. "Rutherford, New Jersey is British?"

"Oh, well, you know what I mean," Chris said. "It's the general air of continental polish. For instance, picture Moose in a maroon cummerbund."

"I remember distinctly that Moose wore a maroon cummerbund when he took you to the senior prom last year," I said, "and I thought he looked very nice."

There was the briefest possible pause.

"I forgot," Chris said.

We spent two more days in London in the rain. It rained on the guard at Buckingham Palace, but they changed it anyway. It rained on Westminster Abbey and on Madame Tussaud's Wax Museum and on Fleet Street and on the Old Bailey and on the Ritz Hotel where we had tea and wafer-thin sandwiches on our last afternoon in London.

Next to us, a British couple sipped sherry and discussed the weather.

"Beautiful day, don't you think, Nigel?" the woman said.

"Oh, wizard!" the man said. "Simply top-hole."

"I *do* hope it's as nice tomorrow," the woman said.

It was.

CHAPTER **3**

SATURDAY, JULY 6.
LEAVE LONDON FOR TOUR BY MOTORCOACH THROUGH
SHAKESPEARE COUNTRY AND LAKE DISTRICT
TO EDINBURGH.

We left London in a downpour, shepherded by the Cook's man to the Victoria Coach station, where he loaded Chris and myself on to a bus that was to take us and thirty other American tourists on the three-day trip to Edinburgh.

We settled down in our seats, surreptitiously eying the luggage tags dangling from other people's suitcases in the racks above our heads. Romantic place names such as Hempstead and Grand Rapids abounded.

"You overtipped the bellboy again this morning," a woman's voice behind us said. "There's no sense traveling all over Europe overtipping everybody. It simply makes them despise Americans."

I turned around and, sure enough, it was the couple from Milwaukee. We greeted each other like survivors of some great disaster at sea and introduced ourselves all around. It turned out that they were the Webbermans, he was in paper boxes, and they had a nephew at the University of Michigan whom Chris didn't know.

"You simply must look up Merwyn," Mrs. Webberman said. "I mean, look Merwyn up. Although—may I ask just how tall you *are*, my dear?"

"Six feet one," Chris said.

"Ah," Mrs. Webberman said. "Well, perhaps not."

The bus began to move slowly out of the station courtyard.

"Here we go," Mr. Webberman said. "How about getting one last shot of good old London, Bernice?"

Mrs. Webberman aimed her camera at the window and clicked the shutter. I told Chris to take a last shot of London too, and she did. (Later, when developed, it turned out to be a picture of the station porter standing morosely under an umbrella, a pink plastic rainhood tied beneath his chin.)

FIRST LEG OF TOUR—WINDSOR, ETON, HENLEY,
OXFORD, STOW-ON-THE-WOLD, MORETON-IN-THE-MARSH,
STRATFORD-ON-AVON.

Windsor was a fairy-tale castle with pennants flying from its turrets. An orange tomcat prowled in and out of the sentry boxes, and at Henley the regatta was in full tilt despite the downpour. The spires of Oxford were shrouded in mist and Chris said it certainly wasn't much like the new Natural Sciences building at Ann Arbor. I said it wasn't much like the old Journalism building at Wisconsin either. Swans were floating on the river at Stratford,

Europe without George

but the red-brick theater was ugly, we thought, like a badly-designed contemporary apartment house. The offering that night was *Julius Caesar*, Chris's least favorite play in the world (result of being taken to see the movie version starring Orson Welles at too tender an age), so we decided to tour Shakespeare's birthplace instead. We saw a First Folio in its glass case, open to Act One of *Julius Caesar*.

"Ugh," Chris said. "I can't even look."

SATURDAY, JULY 6.
LEAVE STRATFORD-ON-AVON FOR KENILWORTH,
LICHFIELD, CHESTER, BOWNESS-ON-WINDERMERE.

"I absolutely must buy Moose some sort of present to take home with me," Chris said. "Without fail."

We were in our hotel room in Bowness-On-Windermere. It was after dinner, and outside we could hear the muffled roar of a torrential downpour over Lake Windermere.

"Laundry time," I said, and ran a sinkful of hot water. We hadn't washed a thing since we left Connecticut, and our meager supply of drip-dry underwear had now run out. "Give me one of the capsules."

Chris handed me a red capsule from the plastic box marked "Traveler's E-Zee-Wash Kit." Wilma Vogelsang had presented the kit to us as a Bon Voyage gift because you couldn't get any soap in Europe, she said. The kit also contained, besides the red soap capsules, a plastic clothesline, six tiny plastic clothespins, and a collapsible plastic hanger that you were supposed to blow up, like a beach ball.

I dropped the capsule into the sinkful of warm water, the way it said in the directions. *"The gelatin capsule will immediately melt,"* the directions said, *"releasing a special-formula liquid detergent which will foam into rich, white suds."* The gelatin capsule immediately melted, staining the water a brilliant pink, but nothing remotely resembling foam, suds, or even liquid detergent, appeared. We tried three more of the capsules, but the water only got pinker.

"Thank you, Wilma Vogelsang," I said, pulling out the plug and emptying the sink. "Now what are we going to do?"

"There were masses of bars of soap for sale in the hotel drugstore," Chris said.

"It's closed by now," I said.

"There's this tube of liquid Prell shampoo," Chris said. "I suppose if it's all right to wash your hair with it it can't do any harm to nylon underwear."

The Prell made a nice, thick suds and we rinsed out everything, including our stockings, bras, and panties, and hung them on the plastic clothesline which we had stretched between the window and the towel bar next to the sink.

"I wish we could go to the movies or something," Chris said restlessly when we were finished. "I'm sick of sitting around England rinsing out panties."

"We'll go to the movies when we get to Edinburgh," I said. "Why don't you write some letters? Shouldn't you write to Moose?"

"I suppose," Chris said. "I'll write him a long letter tomorrow, from Edinburgh."

Europe without George

SUNDAY, JULY 7.
LEAVE BOWNESS-ON-WINDERMERE FOR GRASMERE,
RYDAL WATER, GRETNA GREEN, TWEEDSMUIR,
AND EDINBURGH.

        At Grasmere we trooped through Dove Cottage, where a guide told us a story about Sir Walter Scott visiting Wordsworth and his sister Dorothy and getting such a poor breakfast that he walked to town to the Swan Inn and ordered another breakfast and charged it to Wordsworth. After that we all got on the bus again and drove into town where we went to a souvenir shop and bought picture postcards of the Inn, of Wordsworth, of Wordsworth's sister Dorothy, of Dove Cottage, and of Sir Walter Scott.

There was a display of imitation mother-of-pearl tie-clasps with men's names outlined in gold wire on the counter.

"They're only a shilling each," Chris said. "It's a shame not to buy a few."

"The thing is, do we know anyone named Trevor?" I said.

"Or Wilf," Chris said.

A party of Australian Boy Scouts came into the shop and started to buy postcards. The Boy Scouts were dressed in Bermuda shorts, khaki shirts, and knee socks, and they were all suntanned. Their average age appeared to be about nineteen. One of them was the image of Tab Hunter.

Chris and I gazed at them in awed silence.

"My goodness," I said at last. "The Boy Scout movement in America certainly is still in its infancy."

Europe without George   47

"When I think," Chris said, "of those runty little Scouts in Highmeadow running around tying knots and doing good deeds, I could cry."

SUNDAY, JULY 7.
ARRIVE EDINBURGH SIX P.M. HOTEL NORTH BRITISH.

The Hotel North British was big, fancy, and teeming with ice-water and indoor plumbing. There was a letter waiting at the desk from Moose.

"How is Moose?" I asked, after Chris had finished reading it.

"He's all right, I guess," Chris said. "It's hard to tell, since he has the handwriting of a defective child."

"What news of Highmeadow?" I asked.

"Creepsville, according to Moose," Chris said. "Like living on the moon. Did you find out about the movie tonight?"

"It's Shakespeare Film Festival Week in Edinburgh," I said, "and you'll never guess what's playing."

"Don't even say the name," Chris said. "I can't bear it."

"We'd better stay in and write some letters," I said. "Didn't you say you were going to write to Moose tonight?"

"I mailed him a picture postcard of Dorothy Wordsworth," Chris said. "I'll write him a long letter when we get to Lucerne."

We saw Loch Lomond and the Isle of Sheila and Holyrood Castle and Edinburgh Castle and Sterling Castle and Linlithgow Palace and Bannockburn and the Firth of Forth and Lix Toll, all through a cold, wet curtain of Scottish rain. The guide told us that Lix Toll was as far north as the Romans ever got in Britain.

"They probably ran out of dry socks and went home," Mr. Webberman said sourly.

On our last morning in Edinburgh we got up at dawn because we had to repack everything in order to jam into our valises all the Braemar sweaters and Argyll socks and tartan skirts and Johnny Walker Black Label that we had bought on Princes Street.

"I absolutely must buy Moose a present when we get to Switzerland," Chris said.

The Cook's man called for us at nine. As we trailed after him through the lobby we caught our last glimpse of the Webbermans. Mr. Webberman was wearing a brand new Dress Gordon plaid tam-o'-shanter and reading the airmail edition of the *New York Times*. Mrs. Webberman was writing postcards.

"When do we leave for Geneva?" I heard Mr. Webberman ask his wife.

"Tomorrow," Mrs. Webberman said. "Ten a.m."

"Will we be in Geneva long?" Mr. Webberman asked.

"God, yes!" Mrs. Webberman said. "Six hours."

British European Airways Flight 5375 rose from the rain-slick runway and climbed up, up, up through the thick layer of mist and clouds that covered the Edinburgh airport. At three thousand feet the plane suddenly broke through into clear sky. A shaft of sunlight glinted off the left wing and I involuntarily closed my eyes against the glare.

It was the first sunlight we had seen since leaving Idlewild airport three thousand miles and twelve days before.

CHAPTER **4**

SATURDAY, JULY 13.
ARRIVE LUCERNE. HOTEL ASTORIA

(Note. Accommodation in Lucerne is based on demi-pension
terms and no refund can be made for meals not taken at hotel.)

We sat on the terrace of the Schweizerhof on the shores of Lake Lucerne in the early afternoon sunlight and ate Potage Bouillabaisse; Vol au Vent, Mariniere; Salade Interlaken; Galantine of Fowl, Jelly; Fresh Asparagus; Golden Toast With Raspberries; and Malaga Pudding. After we had finished the Malaga Pudding the waiter wheeled up a serving table with an enormous silver bowl of chocolate mousse.

"— or perhaps the ladies would prefer French pastry?" the waiter said.

Chris and I looked up at him with glazed eyes.

"Jean!" the waiter called, snapping his fingers, and a busboy rushed over and held out a tray of strawberry tarts, cream puffs, charlotte russes, petits fours, mocha tortes, Napoleons, and chocolate eclairs.

Europe without George

I finally took a pastry that looked like a swollen chocolate truffle. When I touched it with my fork it burst open like a firecracker to reveal a stuffing of chocolate, pecans, almond paste, and spongecake soaked in rum. Slivers of glacéed fruit were crammed in and tamped down around the edges.

Chris contented herself with a pastry-and-meringue swan and a fresh strawberry tart topped with whipped cream. The busboy tried to put a dab of whipped cream on my truffle too, but I stopped him.

When we finished our French pastry we sat in silence, staring cobra-like into the middle distance. Somebody's black licorice poodle pranced across the terrace. The sugar-frosted Alps glittered against the horizon. On the far side of the lake, milk-chocolate cows grazed the green marzipan slopes of Mount Pilatus.

A whipped-cream cloud floated lazily across the sky.

"I think I'm going mad," I said.

A waitress brought two cups of cocoa topped with two scoops of vanilla ice-cream.

"Let's go to that candy shop across from the Cook's office and buy some more chocolate truffles and another box of those little peppermint sticks," Chris said.

I reminded her that after lunch we were supposed to take a bus trip up to the Rhone Glacier.

"Well, we could go to the candy shop first and eat the candy while we're riding in the bus," Chris said.

"Or we could just stay in the shop and watch the bus leave from the candy shop window," I said.

We fell silent again.

"That boy looks just like Beast Bessmeir," Chris said,

as a group of young men in lederhosen strolled past, obviously bound for the Lake Lucerne steamer and an afternoon of climbing on Mount Pilatus. "Except that Beast is shorter."

"Who in God's name is Beast Bessmeir?" I asked.

"He's a Beta I went out with last semester," Chris said. "He's a Psych major. He's doing a thesis on the effect of hallucinatory drugs on the nervous system of the American college-age male."

"Lovely," I said. "Where did he get a name like Beast?"

"It's short for Beastly," Chris said.

"Beast," I said. "Moose. Don't you know any boys with good old-fashioned American names, like Bill, or Hank, or George?"

Chris thought a moment.

"Well, there's Dixon St. Clair," she said. "Except, come to think of it, he has a nickname too."

"And what is Dixon St. Clair's nickname?" I asked.

"Lech," Chris said.

"Let's go to the candy shop now," I said.

"Do you think we ought to get a pound of those mocha bon-bons too?" Chris said. "Along with the truffles and the peppermint sticks, I mean."

"That's a marvelous idea," I said.

MONDAY, JULY 15.
AFTERNOON EXCURSION BY MOTORBUS TO
RHONE GLACIER VIA THE ST. GOTTHARD ROAD,
GLETSCH, GRIMSEL PASS, AND FURKA PASS.

I have thought a lot about that trip to the

Rhone Glacier without as yet being able to decide whether the ride up or the ride down was the most terrifying experience of my life. Chris says that the ride up was worse because the bus had a tendency to slip into reverse on the curves, giving one the sensation of being about to plunge backward into an eight-thousand-foot abyss. Also, there was more screaming on the trip up. By the time we rode down most of the passengers could only huddle in their seats, gibbering to themselves or making feeble crosses in the air. I saw one ashen-faced woman at the front of the bus open her purse, take out a black lace chapel cap, and put it on as we hurtled through the Furka Pass.

The only passengers unshaken by either the ride up or down were a family from Georgia—momma, papa, and daughter Shirley Pearl—with three light-meters and six cameras betwen them. Shirley Pearl had a Rolleiflex and a Kodak Instamatic, papa had a Speed Graphic and a tiny Japanese job, and momma was carrying a Polaroid and a Zeiss with a flashgun attachment. Momma also had, dangling heavily from her left shoulder, a mysterious black case exactly the right shape and almost the right size to contain a harp.

The three of them kept up a continuous snapping and clicking and flashing all during the ride, and they didn't slow down much even inside the Glacier itself, which was dark blue and dripping ominously. It cost us five Swiss francs apiece to get inside the glacier and when we came out there were a whole lot of people dressed in Tyrolean costume waiting to sell us postcards and souvenirs.

After everybody had stocked up we climbed back into

the bus again and the driver started off, nose down this time.

"Get some footage on those darlin' houses, momma!" Shirley Pearl cried, pointing to the village of Gletsch a mile and a half below us. "Ah'll get it on the Rollei and papa can get us a color shot on the Yashiwara."

Momma whipped an enormous motion-picture camera out of the harp case, produced a folding tripod from her pocketbook, and set up shop in the aisle, grinding away. The bus careened on down the road at breakneck speed, the driver tooting his horn gaily at every hairpin turn and singing the wedding march from *Lohengrin* at the top of his lungs.

A man in back of me whimpered softly.

The driver broke off in the middle of *Lohengrin* to announce over his shoulder that we were now approaching the exact spot where, in 1960, an avalanche had swept down without warning, killing a busload of Japanese tourists.

"Get that on the Kodak, Shirley Pearl," momma said. "Be sure it's set for infinity."

"Oh, heavens!" Chris said suddenly. "I've lost Moose's fraternity pin."

At that instant another bus appeared around a curve and loomed in front of us. Our driver obligingly swerved over to the edge of the road (it was easy for him to get all the way to the edge because there wasn't any guardrail or fence in the way) a split-second before the two buses met head-on. Our bus swayed for an instant on the brink of the eight-thousand-foot drop, righted itself, and we sped on, both drivers waving merrily to each other.

"I've lost Moose's fraternity pin," Chris said again. "I

had it on this morning and now it's gone."

"Look on the floor," I said.

"I did," she said. "It isn't there."

"Maybe it's on the seat," I said.

We both got up and searched the seat.

"It's gone," she said.

"Well, it must be *some*where," I said. "We'll find it, never fear."

"No we won't," Chris said. "We won't find it because I think I know where I dropped it."

"Where?" I asked. "Where do you think you dropped it?" There was a brief pause.

"In the Rhone Glacier," she said at last, in a small voice.

The driver had switched, I noticed absently, from the wedding march to the anvil chorus from *Il Trovatore*.

"What am I going to do?" Chris said apprehensively. "Moose is going to be furious, especially when he finds out I dropped it into a glacier."

I had a brief but vivid mental picture of Moose's fraternity pin turning up in some crevasse five hundred years from now, along with a lot of rocks, discarded Kodak film, ashtrays engraved *Souvenir Of Grimsel Pass*, and other bits and pieces of marginal moraine.

"We'll report it at the police station," I said. "They must have a Lost and Found department, and if anyone comes across it up at the glacier they can mail it to us."

The Lost and Found department (*FUNDBORO*, a sign over the door said) was tucked away in a blue-shuttered

Europe without George

building in the center of a cobblestoned courtyard bordered with geraniums. Chris and I waited inside the deserted office for somebody to come and help us.

"While we're waiting, look in the book and see if you can find anything about lost jewelry," I said.

She took out *A Happy Trip In All Languages,* turned to the German section, and ran her finger down the column.

"The closest thing is '*Ich mochte ein Photo machen,*'" she said.

"What does that mean?" I asked.

"It means, 'I want to take a picture,'" she said.

"That's not really terribly close," I said.

The door opened and a policeman came in and said something to us in German. We looked at him blankly.

"Sprechen sie Deutsch?" he asked me.

"Non," I said. "I mean, Nein."

He went out again.

"In Sweden if you want a taxi you say *Ring efter enn takhsee oat mee,*" Chris said, still consulting *A Happy Trip.* "In Israel it's *Bahbahdahshah laydahbare yohtare layath.*"

The door opened again and a man in thick spectacles and a long white coat, like a crazed doctor in a science-fiction movie, came in and sat down at the desk.

"Are you two ladies enmeshed in some difficulty?" he inquired, in perfect English.

"Yes," I said. "My daughter here has lost—"

He held up a hand.

"In due time," he said. "First, madame, your passport, if you please."

I gave him my passport. He opened it.

"You claim to be Irene Kampen?" he asked.

"Yes," I said. "I mean, I *am* Irene Kampen."

"And you wish me to believe that this is your photograph?" he said.

"Well, the thing is I had just been to the beauty parlor," I said, "and Jack, who usually does my hair, was sick, so one of the girls . . ."

"Where was this passport issued?" he said.

"In New York City," I said.

"This passport was issued in Bridgeport, Connecticut," he said, in a dead voice.

"I meant Bridgeport," I said. "You see, I applied for it in New York but they mailed it from Bridgeport because Bridgeport is . . ."

My voice trailed away under his stony gaze.

". . . the nearest town," I finished lamely.

"And this is allegedly your daughter?" he said, pointing to Chris.

"Why, of *course* she's my daughter!" I said brightly, giving him the oily smile of a procurer caught smuggling young virgins into Buenos Aires. "Certainly she's my daughter! Christine. My daughter."

He put the tips of his fingers together and leaned back in his chair.

"So," he said. "Now. Exactly what brings you here, madame?"

"Do you mean what brings me here to Lucerne, or what brings me here to the police station?" I asked.

"Yes," he said.

There was a silence.

"Well, madame?" he said. "I await your answer."

I took a deep breath.

"My daughter has lost a piece of jewelry," I said.

"What sort of a piece of jewelry?" he asked.

"A frater—," I began. I stopped. "A pin," I said.

"A *pin*?" he repeated, and sat bolt upright in his chair as though he couldn't credit what his ears had heard. "Do you mean that you have come to the headquarters of the police department of the city of Lucerne, Switzerland, on a matter concerning a pin?"

"It's diamond-shaped," I said defensively, as though being diamond-shaped imbued it with greater significance.

"And it's ebony," Chris said, "with a gold border."

He opened a desk drawer, took out a sheet of paper and a pencil, and handed them to Chris.

"Be so kind as to draw me a picture of this pin," he said. "Just a rough sketch will do."

Chris made a drawing of the fraternity pin and gave it to him. He studied it thoughtfully.

"I see," he said, nodding his head. "Yes. Diamond-shaped. Quite so. And these letters which appear on the pin—what are these letters?"

"Delta Sigma Phi," Chris said. "They're Greek."

"Then the pin was purchased in Greece," he said. "Be so kind as to produce the original bill-of-sale, if you please."

"The pin actually was purchased in the Wolverine Book And Student Supply Store," Chris said.

"Athens?" the man asked.

"Ann Arbor," Chris said. "Michigan."

"And what is the approximate value of this piece of

jewelry?" the man asked, picking up his pencil.

Chris and I glanced switfly at each other.

"Oh, say twenty-five or so," I told him carelessly. The pin had cost exactly eleven dollars (Chris had looked it up in the fraternity jewelry catalogue when Moose first gave it to her), but by now I was ashamed to mention such a niggardly sum.

"Twenty or twenty-five," he said, writing it down. "Pounds, of course."

"Naturally," I said.

He picked up the sketch of the pin and examined it again.

"And what is the significance of these Greek letters?" he asked Chris.

"I'm sorry," Chris said, "but I'm not allowed to tell."

He lowered the sketch and frowned at her.

"Even if I wanted to, I couldn't tell you what they signify," Chris said. "Actually, Moose never even told *me*."

"Moose?" he said.

"Moose is the person who gave me the pin," Chris said.

"Person?" he said.

"Young man," Chris said, lowering her eyelids modestly.

"Ah!" the man said. "And may I inquire why this young man refused to tell you the meaning of the Greek letters?"

"He took a vow," Chris said.

There was a moment's startled silence.

"It's in the rules that they all have to take this vow never to . . . " Chris began, but the man had leaped to his feet and was clasping my hand in both of his.

"A thousand apologies, madame," he said sympathetically. "If I had known that your daughter was enamored of a religious I would not, of course, have pressed her for information."

"Moose isn't—" Chris said.

"No, no!" he interrupted her. "Better not to speak of it any more. But do not despair, mademoiselle—you are young. You will love again."

And with a low bow to both of us he left, shutting the door gently behind him.

Chris and I looked at each other.

"We'd better get back to the hotel," I said at last. "It's nearly time for dinner."

"I think I'm going to have chocolate mousse for dessert tonight," Chris said. "Either that, or a strawberry parfait."

"I'm going to have both," I said.

We sat on the balcony outside our room and read our mail while we waited for room service to send up our dinner. I had a letter from Harry, who said the first officer on our London flight had told him I got hysterical on the trip over and tried to put my lifejacket on inside the plane.

Chris had a letter from the religious, who said there was nothing new in Highmeadow except somebody had dumped the trash cans into the lake again so no swimming for a few days.

The waiter wheeled our dinners out to the balcony. We ate oysters and beef fondue and potatoes Voisin and Romaine salad and for dessert we had chocolate mousse and strawberry parfait. After dinner we watched the Matterhorn turn from pink to violet in the sunset, until finally the sky was black and the lights of the funicular looked like a diamond necklace strung from the top of the mountain.

Then we went to bed.

I woke up in the middle of the night, ravenous with hunger. I reached out to the bedside table, fumbled for the box of peppermint sticks, and ate a couple of them. They tasted awful.

"You've got hold of the wrong box, mother," Chris's voice said patiently through the darkness. "You're eating up all of my safety matches."

CHAPTER **5**

WEDNESDAY, JULY 17.
ARRIVE VENICE BY RAIL SANTA LUCIA STATION.
ON ARRIVAL A GONDOLA WILL BE ENGAGED
FOR TRANSFER TO HOTEL BY WAGON-LITS
COOK'S REPRESENTATIVE.

The Wagon-Lits Cook's representative had patent-leather hair and smelled deliciously of gardenias. He maneuvered us through the throng of passengers and porters out to the wide marble steps of the station, all the while murmuring "Bella! Bellissima!" and casting expressive glances up at Chris.

I sensed that a pinch was imminent.

Once outside, he produced a policeman's whistle from a pocket of his uniform and gave a shrill blast on it. The crowd of waiting gondoliers began to row furiously towards us, smashing into each other's gondolas, making threatening gestures at one another with the gondola oars, and shouting Italian curses back and forth across the water.

The Cook's representative took a pink handkerchief out of another pocket and mopped his perspiring forehead. He then carefully refolded the handkerchief, put it back in his pocket, and said a long sentence to Chris in Italian.

"Ciao," Chris said back. It was something she had picked up from an old Audrey Hepburn movie about Rome.

"What did he say to you?" I asked.

"I think it was something about sex," Chris said.

"I'd love to find out what perfume he's wearing," I said. "It's heavenly."

"Parla Italiano?" the Cook's representative asked me.

I shrugged eloquently, to convey that I had studied the language twenty years ago in Abraham Lincoln High School, Brooklyn, New York, but had forgotten it.

"Your sister, she is very high," the Cook's man said.

"She's not my sister," I said. "She's my daughter."

"Dau-tair?" he repeated. "Please, what is this dau-tair?"

"Me mother," I said, pointing to myself. I pointed to Chris. "She daughter."

"Me Tarzan," Chris said, "you Jane."

The Cook's man reeled back dramatically and flung his arms wide in amazement.

"Impossible!" he said. "You are too young and beautiful yourself to have such a massive daughter!"

I noticed that one of the gondoliers had jumped onto the prow of another gondola that had collided with his and was trying to choke the other gondolier to death. Nobody seemed to be paying any attention to them.

"A beautiful girl," the Cook's representative whispered to me, giving a wink in Chris's direction. "A virgin, one presupposes?"

"Che sera, sera," I said.

The winning gondolier had now leaped back to his own boat and rowed over to the steps where we were waiting. I looked down and saw that his gondola was tastefully furnished with a wicker loveseat and a black leather office chair with ball-and-claw feet. A vase of plastic tulips was fastened to the prow with Scotch tape.

The Cook's representative tossed our valises into the gondola, handed us in after the luggage, and stood on the steps crying "Arrivederci!" and blowing kisses after us as we sailed off.

Our gondolier, who was bald and fat and wore a dirty blue-and-white striped T-shirt, threaded his way through the mass of gondolas clustered around the station, shouting Italian obscenities at his fellow-gondoliers and shaking his fist threateningly whenever another boat blocked our way. We turned into a side canal and narrowly missed colliding with a huge gondola loaded to the gunwales with cases of Pepsi-Cola.

"Che Diavolo!" our gondolier shouted. "Biscoro! Porco mondo!"

The Pepsi-Cola gondolier spit expressively into the water. At that moment another gondola carrying half a dozen female tourists sailed by, and a lady in the prow whipped out her motion-picture camera and began shooting footage of the argument. As our two boats came abreast Chris and I obligingly waved into the lens, and the lady waved back and called over to ask where we were from. We told her we were from Connecticut. She said she and her friends were from Columbus, Ohio, and we all exchanged farewell waves as our gondolier steered around the corner into the Grand

Canal, swerving adroitly to avoid a large garbage gondola that was bearing down on us.

"The Grand Canal!" I said to Chris. "Look—there's the Bridge of Sighs!"

"Not the Bridge of Sighs, Signora," the gondolier said, leaning over and breathing garlic at us. "Bridge of Sighs is more further. This is Rialto Bridge."

"I wonder how come they call the Bridge of Sighs the Bridge of Sighs," Chris said.

"I think it has something to do with Dante sighing at Beatrice when he passed her on it," I said.

The gondolier frowned at me.

"Is called Bridge of Sighs because prisoners going to dungeons would walk across for last time," he said. "They would look out at beautiful city of Venezia and give a big sigh. Like so."

He put his hand over his heart and gave a big sigh, releasing another gust of garlic.

"And there's the famous Ponte Vecchio!" I said, pointing to a bridge ahead of us.

"Ponte Vecchio is in Firenze," the gondolier told me firmly. "We are now in Venezia. Prego."

He went back to his rowing.

"I want to buy some Italian sandals," Chris said, "and a pair of blue sunglasses and a white linen skirt and a yellow raffia sweater."

"I want to buy a gondolier's hat," I said.

"And a present for Moose," Chris said.

A man in a passing gondola stood up, aimed a camera at us, and snapped our picture. He winked at me and tossed a folded piece of paper across the water into my lap.

"Why, mother!" Chris said.

I blushed.

"I guess it's all true about Italian men being incurably romantic," she said. "How exciting! What does the note say?"

I opened the note. It said, "A beautiful black-and-white photograph has just been taken of you and your gondola party. Prints are obtainable at five hundred lire each at the A-One Photo And Souvenir Shop, 14 Via Nazionale."

"Here is Hotel Europa," the gondolier said, stopping the boat at the foot of a wide flight of steps leading up to a dining terrace directly above the Grand Canal.

A doorman hurried forward to help us out of the gondola, which was bobbing and lurching alarmingly in the wake of a passing motor launch. Eighty guests paused in the midst of dinner, forks in mid-air, to watch the debarkation.

"I can't," Chris said, drawing her foot back at the last minute. "I'll fall in, I know I will."

"Andiamo!" the gondolier cried gaily, giving her a little shove.

She shrieked.

"Did he pinch you?" I asked her.

"He pushed me," Chris said.

"Andiamo!" the gondolier cried again, not quite so gaily this time, and gave her another shove. At the same moment the doorman grabbed her arm and, with one last shriek, she clambered out. I followed ungracefully.

"Welcome to Venezia," the doorman said.

Europe without George

The next morning we opened the shutters of our room to a hot, sunny day. We had breakfast under a pink-and-yellow striped umbrella on the terrace over the Grand Canal and watched the gondolas bobbing lazily up and down at their striped moorings while we ate. Directly across from the hotel, the church of Santa Maria Della Salute shimmered in the heat. Every once in a while a motorboat would speed by, carrying a party of bathers bound for the Lido.

After breakfast we cashed a traveler's check and went shopping. We bought Chris a pair of blue sunglasses and a yellow raffia sweater and a pair of Italian sandals and a linen skirt and some dead-white lipstick. I bought myself a gondolier's hat. Then we went back to the hotel and Chris put on the sweater and skirt and sandals and sunglasses and dead-white lipstick and I put on my gondolier's hat and we went down the corridor to the elevator.

"What's on the itinerary for this afternoon?" Chris asked.

"The Doge's palace," I said, "the Basilica of St. Mark's, the Campanile, the Rialto, the Assumption Of The Virgin, and Harry's American Bar."

"Harry's American Bar?" she said.

I took out the little black notebook and opened it to *Venice*.

" 'Harry's American Bar for drinks,' " I read. " *'Be sure to order a couple of Green Noodles. (Hashiwara Kayomoto).'* "

"I know I shouldn't ask," Chris said, "but who is Hashiwara Kayomoto and what's a Green Noodle?"

"Hashiwara Kayomoto is Wilma Vogelsang's part-time

gardener," I said. "A Green Noodle is a cocktail. You know —like a Pink Lady or an Orange Blossom."

The elevator arrived. We stepped in.

"Bon giorno," the elevator operator said.

"Bon giorno," I said.

He closed the doors. The only other passenger besides Chris and myself was a handsome blue-eyed young man with dark hair and the kind of bronze suntan that conjures up immediate visions of Mediterranean beaches, Alfa-Romeos, and a whole lot of money.

Chris fixed her hair.

"I forgot the room key," I said.

"I've got it," she said, and held it up to show me. Italian room keys have great slabs of basalt fastened to them on chains, in case of room-key thieves, and this one now slipped from her fingers and fell to the floor of the elevator with a crash.

"Why, for heaven's sake!" Chris said, wide-eyed. "I've dropped the room key!"

"Permit me, signorina," the young man said, bending down to pick it up and handing it to Chris with a smile that revealed dazzling white teeth.

"Molte grazie," Chris said.

The young man turned and smiled at me too.

"Bon giorno," I said.

"Ah!" he said. "The Signorinas speak my native tongue?"

"Che sera, sera," I said. This was followed by a brief silence, owing to the fact that the signorinas had now exhausted their knowledge of the young man's native tongue. The elevator came to a stop and the operator opened the doors. We were on the main floor.

"I'll meet you outside, mother," Chris said. "I want to stop at the desk and see if there's any mail."

It took her an awfully long time but she finally joined me and we hurried through the winding back alleys of Venice to the Cook's office. The tour was just starting for the Doge's palace when we arrived, but I might as well have stayed right in our hotel room and read about it in the guidebook because the whole time the guide was telling about Pope Julian and Tintoretto and Giacomo Bellini, Chris was telling about Alexis.

Alexis was the young man in the elevator, and it turned out that his home was in Venice, he was a student at the Sorbonne, his father wanted him to go into the family business but he wanted to be an artist, he had a summer job as an art guide for American tours traveling through France and Italy, he was now guiding a tour from Los Angeles, California, he spoke five languages (including Hungarian), he had never been to the United States, the ladies in the tour were driving him crazy because they weren't interested in art and kept asking him the best places to buy Venetian glass, he liked tall girls, he had never heard of the University of Michigan, and he and his Californians were leaving Venice tomorrow night for Rome.

"Isn't that exciting?" she finished.

"Isn't what exciting?" I asked, craning my neck to see the Veronese on the ceiling of the Sala del Senato while the guide explained cynically that the reason it had so many figures in it was because the Doge had made the mistake of agreeing to pay Veronese per figure.

Europe without George

"About Alexis going to Rome," Chris said, "because when you and I get there next week he's going to rent a Lambretta and let me ride on the back seat and take me around the city on it."

"Like Audrey Hepburn in that movie," I said.

"Alexis doesn't care for Audrey Hepburn," Chris said. "He prefers girls with a less pixieish quality."

"What's his favorite hot-weather dish?" I asked. "Or is that the only thing about him you didn't get around to finding out?"

"Shrimp à la Marinara," Chris said. "As a matter of fact, he's taking me out to dinner tonight to have some."

"Incidentally, was there any mail?" I said.

"Mail?" Chris said.

"At the desk," I said. "Where you stopped when we got out of the elevator. Remember?"

"Oh, mail!" Chris said. "Yes, there was a whole bunch of letters. I left them in the box."

"Did you hear from Moose?" I asked.

"Moose?" Chris said dreamily.

"Moose Minifee," I said. "The religious."

"Oh, Moose!" Chris said. "To tell you the truth, I forgot to look."

Hashiwara Kayomoto had tipped me off to Harry's Bar as a big inside secret, but every other American in Venice must have been tipped off too, because the din of voices speaking our native tongue nearly stopped us in our tracks when we walked in. I immediately spotted the gondola full of ladies from Columbus. They had been reunited with their husbands and were now all sitting at a round table in the center of the room. Everybody was wearing gondolier's hats and the ladies had apparently at some time in the afternoon come into close and intimate contact with a Venetian glass jewelry salesman.

Chris and I sat down at a table for two. A waiter came over and Chris ordered a Pepsi-Cola and I ordered a Green Noodle, very dry.

"Very dry?" the waiter said.

"Plenty of gin," I said.

He looked at me with the expression of a man who is forced to deal with nuts all day, and went away.

"Foreigners don't understand the expression 'Very dry,'" I said to Chris. "You always have to explain."

The people at the round table had put their arms around each other's waists and were singing *Carmen Ohio* very loudly. A waiter brought them a fresh round of drinks.

"I'm the owner," a man said, appearing suddenly at my elbow. "You the party ordered the Green Noodle with gin?"

"I'm the party," I said. "What's wrong?"

"We don't usually make them with gin," he said.

"Well, whiskey then," I said. "Whatever way you usually make them."

"No, no, that's okay," the owner said. "You're the boss. You want a slug of gin in it, it's okay by me."

He went away. Some people from Fort Lauderdale had buddied up with the Ohio party and were dragging their chairs and drinks and gondolier's hats over to the big round table.

"Alexis said when he first saw me in the elevator he

Europe without George

thought I was French," Chris said.

I noticed that one of the men who was singing about Ohio's fame in field and game was beginning to cry.

"Alexis said when we both got into the elevator he thought we were sisters," Chris said.

"Alexis is a sweet, sweet boy," I said.

Our waiter came back and put a glass of Pepsi-Cola in front of Chris and a steaming platter of green noodles in front of me. A strong odor of gin rose up from the noodles.

Chris and I looked at the platter.

"I think probably you misunderstood Hashiwara Kayomoto," Chris said at last.

"I think probably you're right," I said.

One of the ladies from Fort Lauderdale and one of the ladies from Columbus had taken off their Venetian glass necklaces and were comparing prices in loud, cross voices.

"Everything okay?" the owner asked, reappearing at my elbow. "Enough gin?"

I picked up a forkful of the noodles and tasted it.

"Just right," I said. "Delicious."

"Pardon my asking," the owner said, "but exactly where are you ladies from?"

"We're from Connecticut," I said.

"Which part of Connecticut?" he said.

"A little town called Highmeadow," I told him.

"Is this Highmeadow by any chance in Fairfield County?" he asked.

"Yes, it is," I said.

"Oh, well, that explains it," the owner said, nodding. "Sure. Fairfield County. I shoulda known."

THURSDAY, JULY 18.
VENICE BY NIGHT—GONDOLA SERENADE.
IN AN ILLUMINATED GONDOLA GATHERING WITH OTHERS
AROUND A GAILY DECORATED BARGE ENTIRELY OUTLINED
IN ELECTRIC LIGHTS WHERE SINGERS AND MUSICIANS
WILL PERFORM IN GAY NATIVE COSTUME.
YOU WILL FLOAT ALONG THE GRAND CANAL. DURING
THE DRIFTING STAGE A VARIETY OF ITALIAN FOLKSONGS
WILL BE SUNG, THE MELODIES SOFTLY REVERBERATING
BETWEEN THE WALLS OF ANCIENT PALACES.
THIS TOUR WILL LIVE IN YOUR MEMORY FOREVER.
2000 LIRE.

"I'm not going," Chris said flatly. " 'Gaily decorated barge!' God!"

"We already have the tickets," I said. "I plan to go and I don't plan to go alone."

" 'Drifting stage!' " Chris said, and shuddered. "It's going to be absolutely ghastly and full of American tourists shriek-ing and giggling!"

"We're going," I said again firmly. "This is our last night in Venice and I want to do something that will live in my memory forever."

"I'm just thankful that Alexis has left," Chris said. "If he saw us I'd die of embarrassment."

The *Venice By Night* trip was scheduled to cast off at eight o'clock, but even though we got to the Cook's office fifteen minutes early there was already a long queue of people waiting to get into the gondolas. The gondolas were bobbing up and down in the water, roped to each other and to the gaily decorated barge. The barge was not only out-lined in electric lights, just like the itinerary had promised, but it also had four loudspeakers attached to it, plus a lot

Europe without George

of artificial flowers and crepe-paper streamers. The musicians in gay native costume were on board and fortifying themselves for the memorable evening with large swigs of Chianti.

Chris and I climbed down into one of the gondolas and settled ourselves to wait for the trip to begin. After a few moments' brooding calculation Chris announced to me, bitterly, that since there were thirty-eight gondolas with five passengers in each gondola we were now roped together to exactly one hundred and ninety-eight other tourists, some of whom unfortunately were beginning to shriek and giggle.

The gondoliers had risen to the occasion by changing into fresh T-shirts, although nobody had gone so far as to shave or use Mum. The gondola we were in was tied directly to the gaily decorated barge so that our gondolier didn't have to do any rowing and was able to spend the whole trip drinking wine from a straw-covered bottle and absent-mindedly fashioning a hangman's noose out of the trailing end of the gondola rope.

As the entire gala procession floated sluggishly down the Grand Canal the musicians kept up a steady blast through the loudspeakers. They began with that old Italian folk tune, *Arrivederci Roma,* and then went on to *Funiculi Funicula, Torna a Sorrento,* and *Santa Lucia.* When they finished *Santa Lucia* they started all over with *Arrivederci Roma* and went through the whole repertory again.

A rival *Venice By Night,* sponsored by the American Express Company, was directly ahead of us in the canal, and the singers tried to outshout each other all evening, only pausing now and then between selections to exchange boos and Italian catcalls across the water.

When we reached the Drifting Stage a bunch of photographers roared up in a motorboat and began to jump from gondola to gondola taking flashbulb pictures of the merrymakers and handing out cards from the A-One Photo And Souvenir Shop. When everybody's picture had been taken the photographers leaped back into their motorboat again and roared away. The Drifting Stage was over.

"Andiamo!" our gondolier shouted suddenly, casting off from the gaily decorated barge and beginning to row like mad. It was obvious that this final phase of the memorable evening was the Dog Eat Dog, or Every Gondola For Itself Stage. All thirty-eight gondoliers unroped their craft from the barge and from each other and streaked off in various directions.

Our particular gondolier reached the Hotel Europa in record time, fetching up at the steps with a splintering crash that soaked all of us with water and brought the doorman on the run. The other three passengers (a party of blue-chinned Argentinians in gondolier's hats who had sat with arms grimly folded all evening) disembarked first. The gondolier handed Chris out of the boat next, and when she was safely on the steps he handed me out too. By this time Chris and I had gotten pretty adept at climbing in and out of gondolas and would utter only one or two short muffled screams when embarking or disembarking.

We stood on the steps and watched the gondola disappear into the warm Venetian night. The American Express and the Cook's barges were only pinpoints of light in the distance now, far off down the Grand Canal.

"I take back everything I said before the tour," Chris said. "Tonight is going to live in my memory forever, after all."

"How come?" I asked.

"I finally got pinched," she said.

"You did?" I said. "I did too."

"You did?" Chris said. "Where? I mean, when?"

"Just now," I said. "Getting out of the gondola."

"Me too," she said.

"Cook's thinks of everything," I said.

CHAPTER 6

SUNDAY, JULY 21.
ARRIVE IN ROME BY AFTERNOON TRAIN FROM FLORENCE.

We traveled down to Rome in a Wagon-Lits car with half a dozen other passengers plus some flies that rode along with us from Florence. The Cook's man who met us at the Rome station shouted "Ahn-*dyah*-mo ahl ahl-*bair*-go!" at the taxi driver, just like in *A Happy Trip,* and we plunged into the brake-screeching, fender-crumpling, bumper-smashing madhouse of Roman traffic.

All hell was breaking loose in the Hotel Continentale when we got there, with people trying to locate their luggage or cash traveler's checks or change their rooms or complain about the air-conditioning in the dining room. It was about ninety-five degrees in the lobby and everybody was milling around and bumping into each other. One group of merrymakers bound for a Rome By Night excursion ("... *continental gaiety, select night clubs, old wine cel-*

lars, 5500 lire per person") got tangled up in the lobby entrance with a large, angry tour that was just arriving from Israel.

"Welcome to Rome," the desk clerk shouted above the din. "Please to surrender your passports. Air-conditioning is twelve hundred lire a day extra."

"I would advise against," the Cook's man said to me. "Is too expensive."

The desk clerk shot him the sort of snarling look you see on the front page of the Daily News under the caption MAFIA LEADER DEFIES BROOKLYN D.A.

"Oh, I guess we might as well take the air-conditioning," I said nervously. "After all, we may never be in Rome again and it will be more comfor—"

"Never be in Rome again?" the Cook's man interrupted in a shocked voice. "Why you say such a terrible thing?"

A man in a wilted seersucker suit appeared next to me at the desk and told the clerk that his name was Schreiner, that he was in 610, and that he had by God been trying to get a pitcher of ice-water sent up to his room for the past hour.

"Sign here," the clerk said to me, shoving the register book forward and completely ignoring Mr. Schreiner.

"Never to see Rome again?" the Cook's man said plaintively. "One could weep."

I signed the register.

"All roads lead to Rome," the Cook's man told me.

Mr. Schreiner, apparently abandoning his quest for ice-water, asked the clerk whether the dining room would be open until nine o'clock.

"Who knows?" the clerk said, shrugging. "Who knows

which of us will still be alive at nine o'clock? You could try."

Outside in the square the Fiats and Lambrettas kept roaring around and around in an endless circle, occasionally smashing into each other. Somewhere far off in the hot night, a woman screamed.

" 'Friends, Romans, countrymen, lend me some ears,' " the Cook's man quoted, hand on heart. "Shakespeare," he explained. "*Julius Caesar*. Very beautiful play."

Chris looked at him.

"I get your room key now," the clerk said to me. He turned to the row of pigeonholes behind his desk.

"The reason the service is so terrible in these Italian hotels is because they're all run by the same man," Mr. Schreiner confided in me. "Fellow name of Albergo. It's a chain, like the Hilton."

The clerk found our key. The Cook's man shook hands with us in farewell.

"You will return to Rome many times again," he assured me solemnly. "Who knows—you may yet have the great good fortune to die in Rome, like Keats. Arrivederci."

"Christina!" someone called as we crossed the lobby again an hour later on our way to dinner. It was Alexis, looking very handsome in a navy-blue blazer, gray slacks, and a blue ascot at the open throat of his white shirt.

"Alexis!" Chris said, and they gave each other a long, intense look, after which Alexis greeted me and told us that his Californians were off on a Rome By Night tour.

"So Gregor and I are free, and would be honored if both of you would join us for dinner," Alexis said.

"Gregor drives the tour bus," Chris explained to me. "He's a darling, if you like black moustaches."

"Here he arrives now," Alexis said.

Gregor, who was built along the general lines of Smoky the Bear, took my hand and pumped it up and down, beaming.

"Gregor has, unfortunately, no English," Alexis said.

"I see," I said. "What does he have?"

"Hungarian," Alexis said.

"That's not so good," I said, "because I, unfortunately, have no Hungarian."

"I will translate for all," Alexis said. "Come, now we will dine."

We crossed the square in front of the hotel, dodging the traffic, and walked down the Via Pretorio to a little sidewalk café. As soon as we arrived the proprietor rushed out with a cry of joy and threw his arms around Alexis, like a passionate scene from *Tosca.*

"Now, now, Carlo," Alexis said, patting him on the shoulder. "Now, now, old fellow."

After he had hugged Alexis some more and cried a little, the proprietor seated us at one of the round tables on the sidewalk under the awning. A waiter came to take our orders. Alexis and Gregor (after a long colloquy in Hungarian) and I ordered Linguini With Clam Sauce. Chris wanted a Meatball Pizza but the waiter looked at her as though she were crazy and said "*Meat*ball? Pizza? Maledetto!," so she told him never mind, she would have linguini too.

"I don't know what he was so excited about," she said

when he had gone away with our orders. "I always have it at the Danbury Pizza Palace and nobody makes a scene."

Alexis asked us how we had enjoyed our stay in Florence.

"It was thrilling," I said, "except two days isn't long enough to see everything."

"Not even two years," Alexis assured me.

"The thing that thrilled us most of all was the statue of Michelangelo's *David*," Chris said. "We took about a dozen color pictures of it."

"Where did you see this *David*?" Alexis asked.

"In the Piazza della Signoria, naturally," Chris said. "Where it is."

"Alas," Alexis said, "you have seen the wrong *David*."

"How come?" I asked.

Because, Alexis explained, the right *David* was in the Gallery of the Academy on the other side of Florence. The statue in the Piazza, according to Alexis, was a copy made after one of the Medicis had dropped a boulder on the original in a fit of temper at the Doge.

"Oh, darn," I said. "And all those color pictures too."

"Hah?" Gregor said, looking at me questioningly.

"The wrong *David*," I explained.

His expression of bewilderment only deepened.

"We saw the wrong *David* in Florence," I said, enunciating slowly and staring with burning intensity into his eyes in the hope of getting through. "Wrong. Bad." I shook my head back and forth. "No good."

"Hah?" Gregor said again.

"I will explain to him," Alexis said, and reeled off a long string of Hungarian while Gregor listened, nodding and beaming.

"This is marvelous linguini," I said, when Alexis had finished explaining. "It's the best I've ever tasted."

Gregor put down his fork again and gazed at me with a hopeful expression.

"Good!" I told him brightly, rubbing my stomach. "Yum."

"Haranyi vleskovik," Gregor said, or something like it. "Mirschi fedanya."

"He says you must come to Hungary someday and taste his specialty, eel hearts in sour cream," Alexis told me. "It's a local delicacy."

"I'll bet it is," Chris said. "Local, I mean."

"Is everyone finished?" Alexis asked us. "Because now I shall have the great pleasure of taking you to see one of the most overwhelming sights in all the world—the Colosseum by moonlight."

Carlo rushed out again to say goodbye, this time hugging everybody in turn, and Alexis paid the bill and we walked to the Colosseum. It was certainly an overwhelming sight and the whole time we were there the conversation went like this:

ALEXIS: The inscription over that portal is dedicated to the Emperor Julius Caesar.

CHRIS: Ugh.

ME: I can hardly believe that I'm really here in the Colosseum.

GREGOR: Hah?

ALEXIS: (*in Hungarian*) She can hardly believe that she is really here in the Colosseum.

GREGOR: (*beaming*) Volgret plemya.

Europe without George

ALEXIS: (*to me*) Gregor says he is happy that the Colosseum makes you happy.

ME: Thank you.

ALEXIS: (*in Hungarian*) She says thank you.

GREGOR: Cracvovna.

ALEXIS: (*to me*) He says you are welcome a thousand times.

CHRIS: I must remember to buy Moose a present before we leave Rome.

ME: (*gazing around*) It's so incredibly beautiful.

GREGOR: Hah?

ALEXIS: (*in Hungarian*) She says it is incredibly beautiful.

GREGOR: Govnoskey escwzir.

ALEXIS: (*to me*) He says he agrees, it is very beautiful.

ME: It seems like a dream that I'm actually in Rome.

GREGOR: Hah?

After a while Alexis gave up and said maybe we ought to get back to the hotel because it was quite late. We walked homeward through the darkened streets, Chris and Alexis holding hands and Gregor thinking long, deep, Hungarian thoughts.

In the lobby we all said good night and Chris and I got into the elevator. Just before the elevator doors closed, Mr. Schreiner came rushing across the lobby and got in with us.

"Whew!" he said, mopping his forehead. "Hot! I'd give two bucks right now for a tall glass of ice-water. Five bucks. You ladies from the states?"

"Connecticut," I said.

"I'm from Pigeon Cove, Maine," Mr. Schreiner said, "and

I wish I was back there right this minute. How'd you folks get to Europe anyway—by plane or by boat?"

"We flew," I said, and made a wide, flapping movement with my arms, like an eagle descending on its prey. "In the sky," I added, and flapped again. Mr. Schreiner recoiled slightly.

"Mother!" Chris said.

With a start, I realized that the evening with Gregor had impaired my powers of communication. I lowered my arms and gave Mr. Schreiner a feeble smile.

"We came on airplane," I said. "—I mean, on *an* airplane."

Mr. Schreiner asked if we had done any sightseeing in Rome.

"Not yet," I said. "Tomorrow we're going to see the Vatican Museum and the Villa Borghese and the Sistine Chapel."

Mr. Schreiner said he had seen them all and to watch out for the Sistine Chapel, it was hell. He said he was only hanging around Rome now because he expected to have an audience with the Pope. He said he had a letter of introduction to the Pope from Herb Klanspranger.

"Herb is the Unitarian minister back in Pigeon Cove," Mr. Schreiner explained. "A great guy. A real *person,* if you know what I mean—not afraid to have a couple of drinks and tell a joke or two when he's out with the boys."

"Does he know the Pope very well?" I asked.

Mr. Schreiner said that Herb didn't know the Pope at all, but being they were both in the same line of work, so to speak, he had kindly written this letter for Mr. Schreiner.

"Never hurts to give it the old college try," Mr. Schreiner

said. "I don't want to boast, but I wouldn't be where I am today in the ball-bearing game if I hadn't been willing to give it the old college try all the way."

The next day we went to see the Vatican Museum and the Villa Borghese and the Sistine Chapel (hot!). The day after that we saw the Pantheon, the Pincio, the Basilica of St. Peter, the Catacombs, and the Forum. The day after that Alexis took Chris to Tivoli on a Lambretta, just as he had promised back in Venice.

On our last day in Rome Alexis escorted us to the station to catch the train for Naples, and promised to meet us in Nice in ten days.

"Now," he said. "Before you leave, one more thing. I must warn you about the Neapolitan men."

"What about the Neapolitan men?" I asked.

"They are terrible," he said. "No woman is safe in Naples."

"We're only going to be there one day," I said.

"No matter," he said. "You must be on your guard every moment."

"Somebody told us that Naples is full of American sailors," Chris said. "The Sixth Fleet is anchored there."

"Compared to the Neapolitan men," Alexis said earnestly, "an American sailor is a harmless child."

"But what do the Neapolitan men *do*?" Chris asked.

"They are sex-mad," Alexis said. "It is the sole occupation of the city. They get up early in the morning and spend the entire day chasing women. They chase them by car and by motorcycle and on foot. They honk at them. They hiss and whistle and wink at them. They also pinch."

"Oh, come now, Alexis," I said.

"It is all true," he assured me. "They particularly like tall American girls. I warn you Christina, if you even pause to tie your shoelace in the street you will be surrounded in a split second by a crowd of sex-mad Neapolitan men."

"Oh, Alexis, you must be exaggerating," I said.

"No," Alexis said. "I never exaggerate."

THURSDAY, JULY 25.
NAPLES.
            Alexis never exaggerates.

FRIDAY, JULY 26.
LEAVE NAPLES FOR EXCAVATIONS AT POMPEII.

            "I like to feel wanted," Chris said, "but that was a bit much."

"Did you have your audience with the Pope?" I asked Mr. Schreiner, who had suddenly bobbed up again on the bus to Pompeii.

"I did not," Mr. Schreiner said. "Never mind," he added darkly. "There'll come a day when the Pope gets to Pigeon Cove and tries to make an appointment with Herb Klanspranger. Ha! Then we'll see!"

Our busload was small, consisting only of Chris, myself, Mr. Schreiner, three American sailors ("Just harmless children," Chris said), and a gum-chewing blonde in spike heels and a clinging white silk dress. The blonde said her name was Mavine and that she was from East Frameville, Illinois.

"That's ten miles outside of Chicago," Mavine said. "A real dump."

Europe without George

The guide took us through the excavations at Pompeii, pointing out the taverns and barber shops and stores of the ancient city. After that he showed us the Museum, and finally he led us to the restored Vetti house, where, he said, two wealthy Roman bachelor brothers had lived. At the Vetti house he made Chris and Mavine and me wait outside in the atrium while he took the sailors and Mr. Schreiner indoors to see some obscene wall frescoes.

"That's a hell of a note," Mavine said. "What do they think we are—kids? Listen, I could tell that guide a couple of things even *he* don't know, believe you me."

"I guess it's a rule," I said. "I don't think they ever allow women to see those frescoes."

"I got half a mind to complain to the American embassy when I get back to Rome," Mavine said. "Of all the nerve!"

When the men came out again I asked Mr. Schreiner, without much hope of an answer, what the frescoes were like, but he only said it just went to prove how decadent those old Romans actually were.

"Aah, them pictures wasn't so much," the little red-headed sailor said. "I seen worse in the Bronx I.R.T. subway station."

SATURDAY, JULY 27.
MOTOR TRIP FROM POMPEII OVER THE BEAUTIFUL
AMALFI DRIVE TO SORRENTO, THENCE BY MORNING
STEAMER FOR CAPRI, VISITING THE BLUE GROTTO.
LUNCH AT ANACAPRI.
RETURN BY STEAMER TO SORRENTO IN EVENING.

Chris and I went out to the balcony of our room in the Hotel Royale for a last look at the black velvet sky and the lighted yachts lying at anchor in the Bay of Sorrento. The air was heavy with the scent of flowers in the gardens beneath us.

"It's all been so beautiful," Chris said dreamily. "The Blue Grotto—and those villas on Anacapri—if only Alexis had been along!"

"That tall sailor and Mavine were in the bar before dinner," I said. "I heard him telling her all about the frescoes in Pompeii."

"The little red-headed sailor asked me to go swimming with him tonight in the moonlight," Chris said.

"That was sweet of him," I said.

"Without any clothes on," Chris said.

Somewhere off in the tropical night someone was strumming *Torna a Sorrento* on a guitar, and just as the great round golden moon rose out of the Tyrrhenian sea, Mr. Schreiner came out on the balcony of the room next door and began to hang his drip-dry underwear over the balcony railing.

CHAPTER 7

MONDAY, JULY 29.
SAIL FROM PIRAEUS ABOARD S.S. ATHENAI
FOR CRUISE OF GREEK ISLANDS OF DELOS, SANTORINI,
RHODES, CRETE, AND MYKONOS.
MEDIUM-TYPE DOUBLE CABIN REQUESTED.

"Excuse me," I said to Chris.

"Excuse *me*," Chris said.

"Sorry," I said.

"My fault, really," she said.

"If you could just sit down on the bed for a minute so I could open my suitcase . . .?" Chris said.

"I can't," I said, "because my suitcase is on the bed and I can't put it underneath until we get the make-up case and the gondolier's hats out of the way."

"I'll take my suitcase into the bathroom and unpack it there," Chris said. "Oh—sorry."

"Ouch," I said. "You stay here and I'll take the make-up case into the bathroom."

"If you're going to open the bathroom door I'll have to go out into the corridor," Chris said.

She went out into the corridor and I opened my suitcase and jammed my clothes into the closet (the Sophocles Steamship Lines had thoughtfully provided three bent wire hangers for each closet). Then I tried to blow up the inflatable plastic hanger that Wilma Vogelsang had given us—its insides seemed to have congealed from the heat—put the empty suitcase under the bed, shoved the make-up case into the bathroom (thereby pretty well filling up the bathroom) and, for want of anything else to do with it, put my gondolier's hat on my head.

"Okay," I called to Chris. "You can come in now."

Chris came in and said she had met two American college boys out in the corridor who were on the cruise only as far as the island of Mykonos where they were going to get off and spend the summer.

"They invited me to stay with them on Mykonos," Chris said. "There's a monastery I could sleep at."

"No," I said.

"It's a deserted monastery," Chris said. "I mean, there aren't any monks left around."

"No," I said.

"You never want me to have any fun," Chris said.

There was a shrill blast from the ship's horn.

"Let's go up on deck and watch the sailing," I said.

It was boiling hot on deck, and the meltemi had begun to blow ceaselessly from the north, just the way *Life* magazine said it would. The Aegean, bluer even than in the travel folders, stretched limitlessly to some invisible horizon. Two passengers were already playing ping-pong under an awning on the promenade deck, and a table of mah-jong was going full blast beneath the striped umbrellas. One man was fast asleep in a deck chair, his bald head gleaming in the sunlight.

Chris and I leaned on the rail and looked down at the Piraeus dock where some taxi-drivers and assorted idlers were lounging with cigarettes dangling from the corners of their mouths. There was a final blast from the ship's horn, the loudspeaker squawked into life, and, to the rousing strains of *Never On Sunday*, the S. S. *Athenai* hoisted anchor and backed out of the harbor. One of the taxi-drivers raised his fist in a Communist salute as we drew away from the dock, but otherwise nobody paid the slightest attention.

The two college boys, wearing khaki shorts and British-Army-type shirts, came over and were introduced by Chris as Sandy and Mike. They shook hands with me politely.

"What would you say to a bit of deck tennis this afternoon?" Sandy said to Chris. "Before the ship touches at Delos, that is."

"Jolly good idea, what?" Mike said. "Top-hole. Well, we'll toddle along now and unpack. Cheers."

"Gung-ho," Sandy said.

They toddled along.

"I thought you said they were American," I said to Chris.

"They are," Chris said. "Sandy goes to U.C.L.A. and Mike goes to Harvard. They act like they're British because they get treated better by the Europeans that way. Europeans look upon American college men as hoplessly immature."

"I see," I said.

Europe without George 107

"Mike knows Dixon St. Clair at Harvard," Chris said.

"It's a small world," I said.

"Mike considers Dixon an absolute fink," Chris said. "Mike says anyone who is willing to spend the entire summer in Paris rather than living on one of the Greek islands is sick."

The loudspeaker squawked on again with the announcement that we were now passing Cape Sounion, crowned with the Temple of Poseidon.

"The really fantastic coincidence," Chris said, "is that Sandy is a Delta Sig."

"Coincidence?" I said. "Why? Does it have something to do with the Temple of Poseidon?"

"Delta Sig is Moose's fraternity," Chris said.

"Oh, Moose!" I said. "Good old Moose!"

"I absolutely must remember to buy him a present on one of the Greek islands," Chris said.

The luncheon gong rang.

"We're at table twelve," Chris told me. "It said so on the card on our stateroom door."

The dining salon was gay and airy and bright with the sparkle of silver and the gleam of white linen. Flowers were everywhere. The waiters, in blue uniforms and gold braid, were scurrying around trying to get people seated at the right tables, a string quartet played American show tunes, voices were raised in happy greeting, laughter rang out. A buzz of excited chatter could be heard everywhere throughout the room.

Everywhere, that is, except at table twelve.

Three of the places at the table were already occupied

when Chris and I sat down. Opposite me was a young woman with a bad head cold who turned out to be Miss Kummer from Norwalk, Connecticut. Next to her was her friend, Miss Finebine, also from Norwalk, and opposite Chris was Madame Westphall, a large Austrian lady.

"You haf been already to Vienna?" Madame Westphall demanded, right off the bat.

"No," I said. The waiter began to serve egg-and-lemon soup. "I don't believe we'll be able to make Vienna this trip."

"But you must!" Madame Westphall cried, banging her palm down on the table and setting everybody's soup slopping about alarmingly. "Now! At once! Immediately!"

"Well, maybe next year . . ." I began, but Madame Westphall pointed a finger dramatically into my face and said, again, "Now! At once! For the Salzburg Festival!"

She sounded as though she was about to lead Chris and me to a lifeboat and set us adrift there and then, but instead she merely sighed, shook her head disapprovingly, and began to eat her soup.

"The eggs that were used in this soup must have been spoiled," Miss Finebine said, laying down her spoon. "Greek food is abominable. We were in Athens for a week and couldn't eat a thing except crackers and cheese."

"I cadt taste adythidg," Miss Kummer said.

"Don't eat the soup, Ravenna," Miss Finebine said to her. "You'll only get the runs again."

Miss Finebine and Miss Kummer sat and watched while Chris and I and Madame Westphall ate our soup. Madame Westphall was finished first and began to eat up all the hard rolls in sight.

"I wish you'd look at that man over there," Miss Finebine said. "Disgusting. I bet anything he's a pansy."

I looked around.

"There," Miss Finebine said, pointing to a table where a laughing foursome was sipping wine and toasting each other gaily. "The man in the green ascot. Pansies always wear ascots."

"Are you sure?" Chris said.

"Always," Miss Finebine said firmly. "You can generally spot them by that, especially if the ascots are green. Or blue."

"Or purple," Miss Kummer said. "Ady of those colors."

"In America the men haff all been emasculated," Madame Westphall said, reaching in front of me for a radish. "Hypothetically speaking, uff course."

The waiter took away the soup plates and brought the next course, roast leg of lamb *à la Grècque*.

"My friend and I will just have some clear broth," Miss Finebine told the waiter.

The waiter went away to get the broth and Madame Westphall told Miss Finebine that if she and Miss Kummer didn't want their leg of lamb she, Madame Westphall, would eat it, as she had a stomach like a stallion and could eat anything.

There was much shuffling of plates and Madame Westphall fell to, gobbling away happily.

"The size of our cabin is simply unbelievable," Miss Finebine said. "I intend to write a letter to the head of the line this very afternoon insisting on a partial refund of our

Europe without George

passage money."

The string quartet launched into *Oh What A Beautiful Morning*.

"That busic is too loud," Miss Kummer said.

"Iss not music," Madame Westphall said, still gobbling away at the lamb. "Iss noise. Only Austrians understand music. Greeks haff not the slightest conception of music. Greeks know only two things—to drink and to abuse dumb animals."

"I'b tode-deaf byself," Miss Kummer said. "I cad't tell Elvis Presley frob Gershwid."

She gave a deprecating little laugh. It wasn't much, but it was the first laugh so far at table twelve.

"I wonder who these two empty places belong to," I said.

"Probably people being seasick in their staterooms," Miss Finebine said. "This boat is terribly unstable. It's common knowledge among all the travel agents."

"Here they come now," Madame Westphall said.

We looked around to see the head steward approaching our table with a couple in tow. The couple was the Webbermans.

"Well, well, well," Mr. Webberman said to me. "If this doesn't beat all!"

"Talk about a small world," Mrs. Webberman said. "My stars!"

The Webbermans sat down and Miss Finebine and Miss Kummer introduced themselves gloomily. Madame Westphall gave an imperious nod and went on eating.

"And Karen!" Mrs. Webberman said to Chris.

"Christine," Chris said.

"Of course," Mrs. Webberman said. "Christine.—*She seems to have gotten taller since Scotland*," she said to me, sotto voce.

"I don't think so," I said. "It's the way she's wearing her hair, probably."

"Ah, yes," Mrs. Webberman said. "Very becoming though, dear."

DELOS. THIS UNINHABITED ISLAND IS THE LEGENDARY BIRTHPLACE OF APOLLO AND ARTEMIS. VISITS ARE MADE TO THE TEMPLES, THE PORTICO OF THE BULLS, THE ROW OF NAXIAN LIONS, AND THE MUSEUM.

"In ancient times Delos was considered to be a sacred island," the tour director told us before we went ashore. The tour director was a large, fierce lady built like Attila the Hun. She added, with a warning look around, "It has always been absolutely forbidden to die or give birth while on the island."

We followed her meekly down the gangplank to the small boats waiting to take us ashore. Delos rose lonely and bare out of the calm Aegean, and when we reached land we tiptoed across the sandy beach, awed into silence by the island's almost palpable aura of vanished glory. Suddenly a throng of Greeks appeared from around the corner of a ruin and began to sell embroidered pocketbooks, gift aprons, and Kodak Instamatic Film.

Most of the passengers, crazed by an entire day out of touch with the marts and bazaars of Athens, started to buy everything in sight and could hardly be torn away by the tour director to go see the Portico of Bulls. Mrs. Webberman in particular seemed gripped by the buying fever, and inside of ten minutes had acquired a pair of goat-hide slippers, a dozen dishtowels with a frieze of the Parthenon hemstitched on their borders, and a tarnished medallion guaranteed to have been dug out of the ruins of the Temple of Artemis that very morning.

"Buy that!" I heard her call to Mr. Webberman, who was examining a woven shoulder-bag decorated with embroidered bulls. "Buy a couple. Buy one for Merwyn."

"What the hell would Merwyn do with it?" Mr. Webberman asked irritably.

"He could carry his books to class in it," Mrs. Webberman said.

"Nice earrings?" one of the Greeks said to me. "Nice earrings and necklace, same like worn by Melina Mercouri in *Never On Sunday*? Only two hundred drachmas!"

"I was very disappointed in the Island of Delos," Miss Finebine said, pushing away her plate of tarama salad. "Except for the erotic sculpture the whole place is very much over-rated, if you ask me."

"What erotic sculpture?" Mr. Webberman said, instantly alert. "Where? How come?"

"Just beyond the Court of Bulls," Miss Finebine told him. "Didn't you see it? Positively *lewd*."

"Obscede," Miss Kummer said, and sneezed.

"The guide showed it to us while you and Mrs. Webberman were down at the beach buying dishtowels," Miss Finebine said.

"Oh, *damn!*" Mr. Webberman said bitterly.

SANTORINI. SOMETIMES ASSOCIATED WITH THE
LEGENDARY ATLANTIS, THIS ISLAND HAS BEEN FAMOUS
THROUGHOUT THE AGES FOR ITS WINES. THE
THOUSAND-FOOT ASCENT FROM THE PORT TO THE PRINCIPAL
TOWN OF THERA IS MADE BY SADDLED ANIMAL.

"What do they mean, 'saddled animal?'"
Chris asked suspiciously.

"These donkeys, I imagine," I said.

"I don't like the sound of the whole project," Chris said.
"I should have stayed on board with Sandy and Mike and
played shuffleboard."

One of the donkey drivers hoisted her onto the back of
a saddled animal (the saddle consisting of a very old and
very dirty burlap bag) and I was hoisted onto the next one.
Side by side, we took our places at the tail end of the strag-
gling line of passengers winding their way upward along
the corkscrew road. Far above us the village of Thera
gleamed white against the vacant sky.

The donkeys plodded stolidly onward, now and then
stumbling on the cobblestones, the sun beat down, the meltemi blew ceaselessly from the north, and a swarm of flies
settled down over the caravan.

Suddenly my donkey (probably bitten by an Attic Blue-
Tail Fly) gave a leap into the air and broke into a frenzied
gallop. We raced along the road, overtaking and passing
the rest of the party in spite of my terrified shrieks of
"Whoa!" and "Help!" as I clung to the saddle, crouched over
like Eddie Arcaro, my hair streaming behind me in the wind.

Europe without George

We rounded one last curve at the top of the road where a crowd of villainous-looking donkey drivers was waiting, spitting and scratching themselves and taking swigs out of a wine bottle they were passing from hand to hand. One of the drivers ran forward and grabbed hold of Gallant Fox's bridle and brought him to a halt. I slid down, my legs trembling.

"Ticket," the driver said, holding out a grimy palm. I gave him the ticket the tour director had given me on board ship, good for one round-trip saddled-animal ride up and down the mountain. The other passengers were now beginning to straggle into view and the drivers surged forward and crowded around them, jostling each other for position to collect the tickets.

Chris was the last to appear around the curve of road.

"Ticket!" one of the drivers said, rushing up to her.

"What ticket?" Chris said. She slid down off the donkey. "What's he talking about?" she asked me.

"The ticket the tour director gave you on the boat," I said. "They turn the tickets back to the steamship company and get paid for the rides."

"I'm sorry," Chris said to the driver. "I guess I must have dropped it on the way up."

"Ticket!" the driver said again, louder this time.

"I don't *have* it, I tell you," Chris said to him. "No ticket. Lost. Gone."

The other drivers had now begun to crowd in on us menacingly with an ominous murmur like the Greek chorus in *Medea*.

"Ticket, ticket, ticket!" the driver shouted.

I realized that our fellow passengers had melted away like rats deserting a sinking ship.

"Get out A *Happy Trip* and look up something nice to say to him in Greek," I told Chris.

"I left it on board the boat," she said.

"Diochete Upsala," I said to him hopefully.

"Delta Sigma Phi," Chris said "Upsilon chapter."

By now we were backed up against the stone wall at the edge of the road and the drivers were swarming in closer, still muttering and murmuring. Everybody smelled terrible.

"Ticket!" the driver said, shaking his fist.

"I don't suppose you're on Diner's Club, by any chance?" Chris asked him. Her voice was beginning to quaver a little.

"Hoy!" a voice shouted suddenly from around the curve. "Evoé! Ho!"

The tour director came panting into view on foot ("I refuse to use one of God's creatures as a beast of burden," she had told everyone righteously, down at the bottom of the road) and looking fiercer than ever. She pushed her way through the throng of drivers and demanded to know what was going on. I explained that Chris had lost her ticket.

"Very unfortunate," she said, frowning. "*Very.*"

"Why can't—" I began, but the donkey driver had launched into a torrent of Greek and I subsided.

"This man claims that you are taking the bread out of the mouths of his five children," she said to me. "He says he is at the mercy of rich Americans who know nothing of what it means to earn a few miserable drachmas by the sweat of their brow."

"I like that!" Chris said indignantly. "I'd just like to see him slave away in the Highmeadow Five-And-Ten the way I did last summer to earn a measly—"

"He says that he and his family will starve unless the ticket is found," the tour director went on, ignoring Chris. "One is tempted to weep at the plight of this wretched peasant."

"Why can't I simply *pay* him for the ride?" I said. I opened my pocketbook, and the wretched peasant broke into a happy grin.

"No, no, no," the tour director said sternly. "No cash. That would upset our entire bookkeeping system."

I closed my pocketbook. The wretched peasant shot a furious glance at the tour director.

"However, I have an extra ticket with me," the director said, fishing it out of the pocket of her blouse. "You can sign your name to it so that if anyone finds the missing ticket the company will not be forced to pay for the same ride twice—is that agreeable to you?"

By this time anything would have been agreeable to me, up to and including taking the whole mess back to Forty-Fourth Street and First Avenue and laying it in the lap of the General Assembly.

"Fine," I said. "If you'll give me a pen, I'll sign the ticket."

"I do not carry a pen," the tour director said. "If God had meant for us to go about laden down with odds and ends he would have given us pouches, like the kangaroo."

"I don't have a pen either," Chris said.

Europe without George

"Ah!" the driver said, and, reaching into the ragged folds of his trousers, produced a red ball-point pen.

"Thank you," I said, taking the pen. I signed my name to the ticket.

"Fifty drachmas," the driver said to me.

"Fifty drachmas what?" I said.

"Papermate," the driver said. "Piggyback Papermate."

"He's offering to sell you the pen," the tour director said.

"Forty-five drachmas," the driver said. "Very good buy."

"I'd take it if I were you," the tour director said to me.

"But I've already *got—*" I began.

"It's worth it simply for the good will," the director said firmly.

I gave the driver forty-five drachmas and he gave me the Piggyback Papermate.

"It really is rather a bargain," the tour director said. "I understand they're next to impossible to get in the United States."

The waiter served us Moussaka Arni Psito.

"The most revolting thing happened to Sandy this morning while the rest of us were on Santorini," Chris said. "It got sort of rough in the harbor and he didn't feel well so he went down to his cabin and stuck his head through the porthole to get some fresh air and a man on the top deck was leaning over the rail and he threw up right on Sandy's head."

There was a brief silence.

"Iff no one iss going to eat their Moussaka, I will take it," Madame Westphall said.

CRETE. THE MOST IMPORTANT ISLAND IN GREECE AND SITE
OF THE ANCIENT MINOAN CIVILIZATION. A VISIT IS
MADE TO KNOSSOS AND THE PALACE OF KING MINOS.

"—through the processional corridor," the tour director
said. "Here we see the famous fresco depicting the bull
dancers."

"Just like in *The King Must Die*," somebody said, for
about the fiftieth time that afternoon.

"I beg your pardon," Miss Finebine said to the man in
the green ascot. He was standing in front of the fresco and
gazing at it. "If you could move over just a *teensy*—so kind."

"What happened to all the gold stuff?" Mr. Webberman
asked the tour director.

Miss Finebine's flashbulb flashed and she clicked the
shutter just as Mrs. Webberman moved directly in front of
the fresco. Miss Finebine said something under her breath.

"All what gold stuff?" the director said to Mr. Webberman.

"The stuff that turned into gold when the king touched
it," Mr. Webberman said.

"What king?" the director asked, eying Mr. Webberman suspiciously.

"That king who lived here," Mr. Webberman said. "The
one you've been talking about all afternoon. Midas."

"Mi - nos," the director said, enunciating carefully as
though she were speaking to a three-year-old. "Not Midas.
Mi - nos."

"Oh," Mr. Webberman said. "Minos. I see."

"As in Minoan," the director said. "Or Minotaur."

"Like in the book *The King Must Die*," the man in the

green ascot told Mr. Webberman.

"I saw the show," Mr. Webberman said. "The road company came to Milwaukee. A great musical. That scene where Yul Brunner dances with—"

"That was *The King And I*," Mrs. Webberman said impatiently. "Can't you ever get anything right?"

"My feet hurt," Mr. Webberman said.

"I finally bought a present for Moose," Chris said at dinner. "I got it in that shop on the palace grounds. Look!"

"What are they?" I asked.

"Authentic genuine Minoan cufflinks," Chris said.

"Minoan *cuff*links?" I said.

"Well, naturally they weren't cufflinks to begin with," Chris said. "They were pieces of some ancient thing dug up out of the palace courtyard and made into cufflinks. See the design?"

"A lovely desigd," Miss Kummer said, examining them. "Phallic, but lovely."

"Very nice," Miss Finebine said. "They have the exact same thing in Bloomingdale's, you know."

"Oh, really?" Chris said. "No, I didn't know."

"Not the New York Bloomingdale's," Miss Finebine said. "The branch store in Stamford, Connecticut."

RHODES. AN IMPORTANT PORT IN ANCIENT TIMES, SITE OF THE FAMOUS COLOSSUS. THERE IS A VERY ATTRACTIVELY SITUATED ACROPOLIS, PLUS FACILITIES FOR BATHING ON THE BEACH OF LINDOS.

The tour director said that those who wanted

to climb the Acropolis would be amply rewarded at the top by the ruins of the temple to Pallas Athena and one of the most exotic views in all Greece.

The thermometer under the awning of the café on the square read ninety-eight degrees fahrenheit.

"Those who do not wish to climb may go to Lindos and swim," the director said. "Those who wish neither to climb nor to swim may remain here in the square."

"I'll see you later," I said to Chris. "I'll meet you back here at this same table in an hour."

"All right," Chris said. "Sandy and Mike and I are going swimming."

"I can't understand why Mr. Webberman decided to climb the Acropolis," Sandy said. "He told me after Knossos that he wasn't going to walk uphill anywhere else in Greece, no matter what."

"I know why," Chris said. "He thought the tour director said erotic view."

"What do you think of this shot I got of Hy on top of the Acropolis?" Mrs. Webberman said, passing a photograph around the table. It was a Polaroid snapshot of Mr. Webberman, in sunglasses and Bermuda shorts, leaning gingerly against the temple to Pallas Athena.

"It's very good," I said.

"Hy came out all right," Mrs. Webberman said, "but I think the Acropolis looks terrible."

"You can always crop out the Acropolis," Mr. Webberman said. "Hey—get it? Crop out the Acropolis! That's pretty funny."

"My friend and I would like two soft-boiled eggs instead of this whatever-it-is," Miss Finebine told the waiter.

"I haff a dream last night," Madame Westphall announced to the table at large. "I dream the Acropolis in Athens iss made from Nesselrode pudding. You know Nesselrode pudding?"

Everybody said they knew Nesselrode pudding.

"Iss all Nesselrode pudding," Madame Westphall went on. "Acropolis, Parthenon, everything—Nesselrode pudding. And standing at the top, in front of the Erectheum, iss Horst Bucholz, handing out spoons."

"Standing in front of the *what?*" Mr. Webberman said, after a moment. "What was that you said he was standing in front of?"

"The Erectheum," Madame Westphall said.

"The Erectheum is a temple to the tutelary deities of Athens," Miss Finebine said. "It is noted for its Classic Ionic architectural style."

"Oh," Mr. Webberman said, and began to eat his soup listlessly.

MYKONOS. THE PICTURESQUE WHITE TOWN CONTAINS SEVERAL CHURCHES AND WINDMILLS, AND TWO PELICANS. THE NATIVE POPULATION OF THE ISLAND CONSISTS OF SMALL TRADESMEN AND WOMEN WHO DO AUTHENTIC GRECIAN HANDIWORK AND EMBROIDERY.

"They certainly look poor," I said. "Wandering around that way with no shoes on and so thin and their hair hanging down. And that girl coming toward us—whatever is she wearing? It looks like a burlap sack made into a

Europe without George

shift or something. Poor thing!"

"Mike Rogers!" the girl coming toward us cried happily. "I can't believe my eyes! What are you doing here?"

"Selma Casdorp!" Mike said. "What are *you* doing here?"

"But we're living on the island for the whole summer, pet," Selma said. "Myself and Francesca and Boo and Liane—why, half of Radcliffe is here."

The ship's whistle sounded.

"We'd better get back to the boat," I said to Chris.

"It's a cultural exchange thing," Selma told Mike. "We're swapping ethnic folk music with the natives. There's a bunch of sociology majors from Barnard here too, but they're impossible."

The ship's whistle sounded again.

"Goodbye, boys," Chris said to Sandy and Mike. "Have a great summer."

"Goodbye," Sandy and Mike told us. "It's been wonderful meeting you both. Happy landings."

"You couldn't have come at a better time," I heard Selma Casdorp tell Mike as Chris and I walked away. "Tomorrow night is the first Hootenanny and we're having the most *awful* time translating *We Shall Overcome* into Greek . . ."

"Now, remember," Mrs. Webberman said, "if you're ever in Milwaukee, you absolutely must remember to look us up."

"Oh, we will," I said. "I've got your address written down and everything."

"And when Katherine gets back to Michigan she really ought to get in touch . . ."

"Christine," I said. "Oh, she will. Merwyn Webberman.

I'll remind her before she leaves."

"Oh, I will," Chris said to Mrs. Webberman. "The very first minute I have a chance, I will."

"You'll like Merwyn," Mrs. Webberman told her. "He's a little shy at first, but after you get to know him he's terribly amusing. What was that he said that was so funny when we were all at Oscar's wedding, dear?" she said to Mr. Webberman. "You know—something about the orchestra? A pun of some sort?"

"Oscar who?" Mr. Webberman said.

"Your *brother* Oscar," Mrs. Webberman said, with a trace of acidity.

It was the Captain's Gala Dinner, the last night of the cruise. Everybody was wearing paper hats, and there was a noisemaker at each place.

"Iss my hat on straight?" Madame Westphall asked. She was wearing a crown made out of gold foil with paste diamonds set around its border.

"I remember now," Mrs. Webberman said. "He said that the orchestra was all right but that Meyer Davis didn't need to lose any sleep at night over it."

The lights in the dining salon were suddenly dimmed, and the orchestra played a fanfare.

"It was the way Merwyn said it," Mrs. Webberman said. "This sort of dry turn of speech he has, I mean. You have to hear him to appreciate it."

"Iss Meyer Davis Jewish?" Madame Westphall asked.

The double doors of the dining salon were flung open. A dozen or more waiters marched in, bearing silver trays over their heads, and on each tray was a silver bowl flaming with the blue, dancing fires of a brandy sauce. The procession of waiters marched around the room twice while the orchestra played *Pomp and Circumstance* and then the waiters lowered the trays and moved towards their individual tables. The lights came on again, the din of voices rose to a new crescendo, the room was filled with the clink of champagne glasses, the buzz of excited laughter, the strains of a gay Viennese waltz.

"It was the way he said it," Mrs. Webberman said. "You have to know Merwyn to appreciate how funny he sounds when he says anything humorous."

Our waiter began to serve the flaming, honey-dripping, meringue-smothered Cherries Jubilee Flambée *au Attica*.

"Do you by any chance have a little lime sherbet?" Miss Finebine asked him.

CHAPTER **8**

TUESDAY, AUGUST 6.
LEAVE ATHENS AT 10:30 FOR FLIGHT TO NICE.

The Mediterranean surf foamed over the white-pebbled shore of the Bains des Plages on the beach at Nice. Just behind us was the great curve of the Promenade des Anglais, lined with hotels that looked like elaborate wedding cakes fluted with pink icing. Tricolored flags fluttered and snapped in the ocean breeze.

". . . straight up the dormitory wall like some sort of a human fly," Chris said. Chris was telling Alexis about a pantie raid at Michigan (Alexis never tired of hearing about intellectual life in the Big Ten and would listen, entranced, for hours—"What is a Deke? This course you took—Great Apes? What is that? Oh, I see. Of course. Anthropology.")

The clink of glasses came from the direction of the bar under the cool shadows of the boardwalk. Toylike pedalboats dotted the water near the shore, and farther out somebody's yacht rode at anchor beneath the cloudless sky.

"How was it possible for him to scale this wall?" Alexis asked Chris. "Did he wear crampons?"

"He was a Rotcie," Chris said, "and they learn how to climb cliffs and things in the dark so naturally Markley Dormitory was child's play to him."

All over the beach people were reading the morning newspapers with expressions of severe disapproval on their faces. The so-called Chicken War had broken out on the day we arrived in France and the headlines were bristling with nasty cracks at *Les États-Unis*.

"A Rotcie?" Alexis said to Chris.

"R.O.T.C.," Chris said. "Reserve Officers Training Corps."

"Ah," Alexis said. "Officers. I see."

Next to Alexis a girl was sun-bathing face-down without the top of her bikini on, although it was right there on the sand next to her where she could get at it quickly in case of fire or anything. She was wearing the bottom half, which wasn't much of a muchness to begin with, and a string of pearls.

I glanced at Alexis, but he was completely absorbed in the pantie-raid saga.

". . . housemother came screaming in," Chris was telling him, "and Beast kept tossing the panties down to this absolutely howling mob in the courtyard and a photographer from the *Detroit Free Press* was snapping pictures. It was like something out of the French Revolution."

"Les Américains sont sauvages," a man under an umbrella in front of us said to his wife, angrily rattling his copy of *L'Éclaireur de Nice et du Sud*. "Regarde, s'il vous plaît, M. Orville L. Freeman. Pah! Je m'en fiche d'Orville L. Freeman!"

"To make everything perfect I was studying for Rat Lab like a mad thing and . . ." Chris said, and then her voice trailed off in mid-sentence because the girl next to Alexis sat up, yawned, and leisurely began to put on the top of her bikini. When she had it half on she ran into some sort of hook-and-eye trouble and she took it off again, examined the strap, and put it on once more.

"What is this Rat Lab?" Alexis asked Chris, who was still gazing open-mouthed at the girl. "Is it some sort of a course offered by the University authorities?"

The girl now stood up and ambled down to the water.

"Rat Lab?" Alexis said again. "Could you explain, please?"

"Psychology Laboratory," Chris said absently. "Alexis, didn't you see that girl?"

"Which girl?" Alexis said.

"The one right next to you," Chris said. "The one who just went into the water."

"No," Alexis said. "I mean, yes. I guess so. What about her?"

"What *about* her?" Chris said. "Why, she was lying there without any top to her bathing suit and when she got up she put it on in front of everybody!"

"Oh yes," Alexis said.

"Practically in your *face*!" Chris said.

"So?" Alexis said, politely.

"And you hardly even noticed!" Chris said.

"Should I have?" Alexis asked, looking bewildered.

"Well, I never knew anybody before who could just sit

there while a person put on their bathing suit in front of him and not even turn a *hair!*" Chris said.

"It is only the human body," Alexis said. "A perfectly natural phenomenon."

"Not in Highmeadow, Connecticut, it's not," Chris said.

"European men regard these things differently," Alexis said, waving a casual hand around at the beach full of bikini-clad females, a large number of whom had mislaid their bathing suit tops in the sand. "Feminine nudity on the seashore does not excite us."

"It doesn't?" Chris asked.

"Not even faintly," Alexis assured her.

"I see," Chris said, and fell into a thoughtful silence.

"What shall we do now?" Alexis said. "Shall we go out in one of those pedal-boats together?"

"I just remembered something I forgot at the hotel," Chris said. "You go ahead and have a swim and when I get back we'll go out in the pedal-boat."

Chris left and Alexis went swimming and I stretched out for a nap in the sun. The last thing I heard before I drifted off was the *Éclaireur de Nice* man damning Orville Freeman some more. When I opened my eyes again Alexis was drying himself off with a towel, and then he sat down and began telling me about the new tour he was going to be assigned to in Paris.

"It is a group known as the Contract Bridge Association Of Northern Westchester County," Alexis said, "the meaning of which I am still not quite clear about in my mind."

"Don't even try, Alexis," I said.

"I understand that they are touring the continent on a

Europe without George

large bus with their wives and their . . ." Alexis said, and then his voice trailed off in mid-sentence just the way Chris's had done earlier. His jaw dropped and he made a strangled sound in his throat. I followed his gaze and saw Chris coming toward us, wearing a white bikini. There seemed to be a great deal of Chris and very little of bikini.

Alexis got slowly to his feet.

"Do you like it?" Chris asked me. "It was on sale at the hotel shop. I saw it yesterday but I didn't have the nerve to buy it until Alexis said what he did about how it's a perfectly natural phenomenon and everything."

"What *size* is it?" I said.

"They don't come in sizes," she said. "They came in small, medium, and large. This is medium."

"I'd give a pretty to see the small," I said.

"They had them in black and in white," Chris said, "but I thought white was more . . ."

"Mon Dieu!" the *Éclaireur de Nice* man said, looking up and spotting Chris standing there.

". . . youthful," Chris said.

The *Éclaireur de Nice* man tossed aside his paper, obviously willing to forget all about the Chicken War and any other little Common Market disagreements between America and France. The pedal-boat boy and one of the lifeguards had now edged up to our little group and were also staring goggle-eyed at Chris.

"Well, Pamela, mother *does* consider it shocking," an Englishwoman somewhere nearby said, in the loud, carrying voice that did so much to help the British lose India. "Mother would certainly never permit you to appear in public wearing a bathing suit like that, dear."

"Voici l'Américaine!" the pedal-boat boy said to his companion. "Comme elle s'élève!"

I was beginning to feel like a State Department courier in charge of some sort of traveling exhibit on the scale of the Washington Monument.

"I don't understand what everybody's so upset about," Chris said, finally sitting down. "Especially you, Alexis. You yourself told me that European men aren't even faintly excited by you-know-what."

"I said that?" Alexis said.

"You certainly did," Chris said.

"I must have been out of my mind," Alexis said firmly.

"It's exactly the same sort of Bikini that every French girl on this beach is wearing," Chris said.

"It's just that you look so—so—" Alexis said, and swallowed.

"Yes?" Chris said. "I look so—?"

"So *American*," Alexis said, and sat down next to her. "Charming!" he added quickly. "Charming and very beautiful, but entirely American."

"Speaking of Americans, you'll never guess in a million years who I bumped into right on this beach," Chris said to me.

"Orville L. Freeman," I said.

"Dixon St. Clair," she said. "He said he'd come over and say hello to you. He's with the most fantastic girl—blonde hair down to her waist and eyelashes two inches long."

"She sounds like Brigitte Bardot," I said.

"Actually her name is Mary Ann Sauerwine from Vassar," Chris said. "She's an Experiment In International Living."

"Here they come now," I said.

Alexis stood up.

"Hello again," Dixon said to Chris. "Hello, Mrs. Kampen. Terribly nice to see you once more."

Chris introduced Alexis, and he and Dixon shook hands.

"And this is Mary Ann Sauerwine," Dixon said.

"Hah theah," Mary Ann said in jasmine accents, batting the eyelashes at Alexis.

"Mary Ann is living with a family in Paris for the summer," Dixon said. "She's learning the French language and the customs of the country."

"The strangest thing happened while we were walkin' over heah," Mary Ann said, wide-eyed. "We passed a lady under an umbrella and she was the spittin' image of mah cousin Emmeline back in Memphis!"

"Never mind, Mary Ann," Dixon said. "Forget it."

"I met a friend of yours in Greece," Chris told Dixon. "Mike Rogers from Harvard."

"I know Mike Rogers," Mary Ann said. "Mike Rogers is a livin' doll. Those blue eyes!"

"Contact lenses," Dixon said. "Rogers is constantly popping them in and out when we're eating in Commons. Terribly crude."

"Now, sweetie," Mary Ann said. "Don't be mean. I think Mike Rogers is the livin' image of Rip Torn."

"Rip Torn?" Alexis said. "Who is this Rip Torn?"

"A movie actor," Chris told him.

"Which hotel are you staying at?" Dixon asked me.

"The West End," I said. "It's that big one right across the street. See?"

"Well say, if that doan look just like Lathrop Hall back at Vassar!" Mary Ann exclaimed. "My land!"

"Are you a University man?" Dixon asked Alexis.

"Yes, I am," Alexis said. "The Sorbonne."

"The Sor*bonne*?" Mary Ann said. "Are y'all an Exchange Student?"

"I am Italian," Alexis told her. "My home is in Venice."

"Venice!" Mary Ann said, giving the eyelashes another workout in Alexis's direction. "How thrillin'! That's how come you're so suave and continental, I bet."

Alexis blushed fiercely.

"Ah'm 'bout to swoon just *lookin'* at you," Mary Ann said. "Venice! Why, that's the most romantic thing I evah heard of."

"Okay, Mary Ann," Dixon told her. "Simmer down now. Just relax."

"You are the *absolute* livin' image of Troy Donahue," Mary Ann said to Alexis, completely ignoring Dixon, "and I happen to think Troy Donahue is the best-lookin' thing on earth."

"Troy Donahue?" Alexis said.

"Mah dream man," Mary Ann assured him.

"All right, Mary Ann," Dixon said patiently. "Come along now and I'll buy you some lunch. Say goodbye to the people."

" 'Bye, you-all," Mary Ann said. "It's been fun."

"Cheerio," Dixon said to us, taking Mary Ann by the arm. "Maybe we'll see each other again in Paris."

"'Bye, sweetie," Mary Ann called over her shoulder to Alexis. "—mah goodness but that Chris is *tall!*" she said to Dixon as they walked away. "And wearin' such an itty-bitty little old bathin' suit, too. Great big girls like that always make me feel so *teeny* . . ."

"You can sit down now, sweetie," Chris said to Alexis.

Alexis sat down, looking rather dazed.

"Who is this Troy Donahue?" he said.

"He's another movie actor," Chris said. "He's blonde and he's got a crew-cut, but otherwise you're the absolute living image of him, you-all."

"Now, sweetie," I said to Chris. "Don't be mean, sweetie."

"This Mary Ann Sauerwine," Alexis said. "Are there many like her in America?"

"It's one of our national hazards," Chris said.

"If I were St. Clair I would go mad," Alexis said. "However, one must admit that she *does* resemble Brigitte."

"Brigitte?" Chris said.

"Brigitte Bardot," he said. He got up and pulled Chris to her feet. "Come," he said. "I will take you for a ride in a pedal-boat, bikini and all."

"First explain one thing to me," Chris said.

"Yes?" Alexis asked. "What would you like explained?"

"Who is this Brigitte Bardot?" Chris said innocently.

SATURDAY, AUGUST 10.
LEAVE NICE BY AIR FRANCE (FLIGHT 0017)
FOR ORLY AIRPORT, PARIS.

"Air France passengers arriving on Flight 0017 from Rome and Nice kindly claim your baggage on the lower level," the girl on the P.A. system announced sexily, sounding just like Edith Piaf.

The porters who were lined up at the baggage conveyor belt looked like a male chorus line in their fitted slacks and blue sports shirts. The strains of *La Vie en Rose* were now coming over the P.A. system, and the women waiting for their luggage on either side of me gave off great gusts of Arpège.

The first thing that came down the conveyor belt was a crate containing two yowling Siamese cats. This was followed by a lot of expensive-looking suitcases, and then by another crate with a white poodle in a diamond-studded collar. Our luggage appeared last, as usual.

"Have I the pleasure of addressing Madame Kampen?" a Cook's man said, approaching at a little run and gallantly sweeping off his cap. "Allow me—Jean-Louis Brun, at your service."

"How do you do, Mr. Brun," I said. "This is my daughter Christine."

"Enchanté," the Cook's man said, grabbing Chris's hand and kissing it. He was dark and handsome, although a bit red-rimmed around the eyes, and he wore his hair in a wavy, backward sweep. There was a plastic spray of lily of the valley in his buttonhole. "I have the honor to escort you to your hotel. Follow me, if you please."

We trailed him out to the taxi stand where he bundled us into a tiny cab and climbed in after us, settling himself on the jump seat and fixing a burning gaze on my legs.

"A l'hôtel Astorg," he told the driver over his shoulder. Then, leaning forward until he was practically in my lap, he said, "Parlez français, Madame?"

"Not terribly well," I said, with a nervous laugh.

"Vous avez les jambes très élégantes," he said meaningfully, and gave a tremendous wink.

"What was that he said?" I asked Chris.

"He said you have very elegant legs," Chris said. "Frankly, I think he's some sort of a sex maniac. Listen to the way he's breathing."

"I can hardly believe we're really in Paris!" I said to Chris brightly, peering out the window and trying to edge as far away from Jean-Louis as possible, not easy in a cab that size. "Look—the Eiffel tower! How thrilling!"

"Paris is a city of one thousand thrills," Jean-Louis said, gazing into my eyes, "but a beautiful woman is the most thrilling of all, n'est-ce pas?"

"This boy is a nut," I said to Chris sotto voce.

"Will Madame permit an observation?" Jean-Louis said to me. "Her hair is *ravissant*—black like the wing of the eagle."

"Raven, I think he probably means," Chris said.

"Madame has a husband?" Jean-Louis asked me.

"No," I said.

"The husband, he is dead?" Jean-Louis asked.

"I'm divorced," I said. "*Divorcée.*"

"A - *ha!*" Jean-Louis exclaimed, and gave me another enormous wink.

The cab came to a stop and the driver said that we had arrived at the hotel and that somebody owed him twenty francs.

"It's certainly been nice meeting you," I said to Jean-

Louis, hastily getting out of the cab. Chris followed me. "Goodbye now."

"But you flee!" Jean-Louis said, leaping out of the cab after us. "You run away like a—how do you say in English—some small animal—?"

"Hamster?" Chris said. "Squirrel? Mouse?"

"Mouse," Jean-Louis said. "Merci."

"Pas de quoi," Chris said.

"Twenty francs," the driver said.

"You must not be afraid of *l'amour*," Jean-Louis said earnestly as we all stood on the sidewalk in front of the hotel at nine o'clock in the morning. "As we say in France, *Il n'y a que le premier pas qui coûte.* Do you understand what this means?"

"You bet," I said. "Well, goodbye again—"

"I shall accompany you to your room," Jean-Louis said. "—Only, of course, to assure myself that all is well with the accommodations," he added, and winked again.

"No, no, it's not necessary," I said. "I'm sure everything is just fine."

"Twenty *francs*," the driver said again, in a bored voice.

I dug some money out of my purse and gave it to him.

"At least share a small *apéritif* with me," Jean-Louis pleaded. "My apartment is only a block away—we can be transported there in a moment."

"It's out of the question," I said. "Napoleon's Tomb at ten, and it's after nine now."

"Napoleon's Tomb?" Jean-Louis said.

"The morning Cook's tour of Paris," I said. "It's right here on our itinerary—see?"

"You prefer Napoleon's Tomb to an hour of *l'amour*?" the Cook's man said in disbelief.

"Oh, *yes!*" Chris and I chorused fervently.

"It is to render one speechless," he said. He climbed sadly back into the cab. "Au revoir," he told us, and waved through the window, shaking his head in regret.

"Les Américains sont sauvages," I heard the cab driver say to him comfortingly as they drove off.

It had a familiar ring.

We not only saw Napoleon's Tomb, we also saw the Élysée Palace, the Eiffel Tower, the Place Vendôme, Versailles, Notre Dame, the Latin Quarter, the Palais de Justice, and the Arc de Triomphe. We even took a trip on a Bateau Mouche, floating down the Seine in an iridescent glass bubble all ashimmer with candlelight, music, champagne, caviar, and a pink Parisian sunset.

On our next-to-last night in Paris we looked in the little black book and found the name of a restaurant that Moose's fraternity brother's father's business partner had recommended.

"It's kind of small and out of the way," Moose's fraternity brother's father's business partner had said, flicking ashes from his expensive cigar, "but as far as I'm concerned they serve the best food in Paris."

"Can you tell us how to get to this place?" I asked the concierge at the hotel. "We've been told it's very good."

The concierge studied the little black book.

"Alas," he said, shrugging. "I happen to know that this particular restaurant is closed."

"Closed?" I said.

"For the entire month," the concierge said. "It will not re-open again until September."

"Well, there you are," Chris said resignedly. "Wilma Vogelsang was right after all. Paris is closed in August."

CHAPTER 9

"This is probably the last time in my life I'll ever be in Paris," I said. "Tomorrow night I'll be back in Highmeadow watching the late show and drinking No-Cal lemon soda, but tonight I want to live!"

"Mmmm," Chris murmured, putting a final coat of pearl nail polish on her toenails.

"Am I destined to be the only American tourist who ever came to Paris and didn't get inside a single cabaret or night club?" I asked. "Am I doomed to spend my final evening in the City of Lights alone in my hotel room?"

"Well, you could come along with Alexis and me, I suppose," Chris said unenthusiastically. "Of course, it's the last time in my life I'll be able to see him, but you're more than welcome."

"Gee, thanks a lot, Goneril," I said. "What do you hear

from Regan these days?"

"I have an idea," she said, "Why don't you take that *Paris After Dark* tour?"

"What's the *Paris After Dark* tour?" I asked.

"It tells about it in the Cook's booklet," she said. "They go to all kinds of cabarets and things and it only costs seventy-two francs, including the champagne." She got the booklet out of my suitcase and opened it. "Listen," she said. " 'Night-time in Paris! More and more lights glow in the darkness, music throbs from a thousand night spots, excitement and gaiety fill the air!' "

"My goodness," I said.

" 'You set off by coach on a round of thrills and de-lights,' " Chris read, " 'visiting famous cabarets including the famous Moulin Rouge and the Pulsating Boule Blanche.' "

"Pulsating?" I said.

"That's what it says," Chris said. "Pulsating."

"I believe I'll go," I said.

"You can wear my artificial eyelashes," she said. "Alexis doesn't like them on me. He says they detract from my na-tural air of American innocence."

She gave me the artificial eyelashes and read some more from the booklet while I put them on.

" 'Flowing champagne!,' " she read. " 'The swirl of the cancan, marvelous floor shows, all the glamour and color of carefree Paris are yours. Our guide will be there to help you savor the magic and see that the coach returns you to your hotel.' " She lowered the booklet and said, ·dreamily, "Maybe the guide will be tall and handsome, like Rossano Brassi in that movie with Katherine Hepburn."

"That wasn't in Paris, it was Rome," I said. "And it was Audrey Hepburn and Gene Kelly."

"Kelly, Brassi, what's the difference?" Chris said. "The main thing is that he was handsome."

The booklet had said that the round of thrills and delight would begin at the Cook's office at nine p.m. Unfortunately, someone at Cook's had turned off all the lights except a lone bulb hanging over the reception desk, thereby giving the office the gala atmosphere of a watchman's shack on the Chicago Milwaukee and St. Paul railroad.

Two couples were huddled under the glare of the single bulb. One of them was the Webbermans.

"Well, say!" Mr. Webberman said. "What a coincidence!"

"Talk about a small world!" Mrs. Webberman said. "My stars!"

The other couple was Australian, the woman gaily attired in a biscuit-colored shirtwaist and health oxfords and her husband wearing a blazer with the emblem of a Melbourne tennis club on the breast pocket. She introduced herself, in the polite, hushed tones of a mourner at a wake, as Mrs. Cleverhausen.

"You can call me Ferdie," Mr. Cleverhausen said. I caught a faint whiff of gin.

"I hope the guide speaks decent English," Mr. Webberman said. "The one we had this afternoon at Notre Dame was so bad I couldn't understand one word he said."

"How is Kathleen?" Mrs. Webberman asked me.

"Christine," I said. "She's fine, thank you."

"We found out about this tour by accident," Ferdie said.

"Came across it in the Book's cooklet." He hiccoughed, and said, carefully, 'I mean, cooklet. *Book*let."

The guide now appeared from some mysterious region at the back of the office and, after shaking his head disapprovingly at the small size of our party, shepherded the five of us to the waiting bus. The guide was short, fat, and heavily moustached, looking absolutely nothing like Rossano Brassi or Gene Kelly.

When we were all aboard the bus he made a little speech in which he outlined the indescribable delights awaiting us this evening. His English was awful. Mr. Webberman kept saying "What? What did he say?" to Mrs. Webberman, just the way he had in London.

"First we visit Montmartre," the guide said, "and indulge in a cabaret where are featured very beautiful young women."

"What was that?" Mr. Webberman said.

"Next we shall take ourselves to the famous Moulin Rouge," the guide said. "Here are displayed an elaborate spectacle and much gay music and singing. The Moulin Rouge is known for the cancan dance, of course, and for the drawings of Toulouse-Lautrec."

"Who?" Mr. Webberman said.

"I implore you to stay together and not wander without me," the guide said. "And now—allons! A la Boule Blanche!"

"I knew it," Mr. Webberman said. "Now he's talking French. It's disgraceful."

The Boule Blanche was located down a flight of steps and behind a dark door. The nightclub was paneled in crimson velvet, with crimson-shaded chandeliers and crimson cloths on the tables. The tables were lined up along both sides of a runway that extended the full length of the room. A bottle of champagne in a silver bucket stood on each table.

The floor show was beginning just as we arrived. The orchestra crashed into *Auprès de ma Blonde,* the lights dimmed, a white spotlight came on, and a dozen girls pranced down the runway, absolutely nude.

"Good God!" Ferdie said, transfixed in his chair.

"Well, well, well," Mr. Webberman said, and he took out a handkerchief and mopped his forehead. "Not much like good old Melbourne, eh, Ferdie, old chap?"

Mrs. Webberman and Mrs. Cleverhausen seemed beyond speech.

The girls lined up along both sides of the runway with one of them—a tall brunette—stationing herself directly above our little group. She looked down at our table absently and scratched a freckle on her stomach. I heard Ferdie and Mr. Webberman sucking at their teeth and breathing heavily, as after a fast doubles match.

The waiter poured the champagne.

"The girls in these shows aren't French at all, you know," Mrs. Cleverhausen said. "They're British."

"How can you tell?" I asked her.

"It's common knowledge," she said.

The waiter poured more champagne.

"It's a wonder they don't take cold," Mrs. Cleverhausen said. "Standing about like that."

The floor show went on for a long time but there really wasn't much variety to the program. The girls pranced off after a while and then the master of ceremonies introduced the next act, which was a blonde who came out fully dressed and did a strip-tease. After she finished the girls pranced out again, and after that the master of ceremonies, and then another strip-teaser, and then the girls again, and so on for an hour and twenty minutes. I imagine that if I were a man and there was such a thing as seeing too many naked women, I would have seen too many that night at the Boule Blanche. However, Mr. Webberman's interest never seemed to flag, and at the end of the show the guide had a terrible time getting Ferdie to leave with the rest of us.

Ferdie wanted to stay right where he was and wait for the next show, which was due to start at midnight. He said the rest of us could nip along and he'd catch up later. He said he'd had a hard day, what with that perishing hall of mirrors at Versailles, and he'd just as soon stay where he was and give the old clipper-cloppers some rest.

The guide finally lost his temper and shouted "Allons!" so fiercely that I thought he was going to launch into the *Marseillaise*. Ferdie reluctantly got up and tagged along after us to the Moulin Rouge, home of the French cancan.

As soon as our bus drew up in front of the Moulin Rouge with its revolving windmills outlined in bright electric lights, Ferdie seemed to forget his foot trouble and to perk up and take an interest in life again. As a matter of fact, Mrs. Cleverhausen had a hard time calming him down. On the way in through the lobby he tried to buy a souvenir program with a gold tassel and, once inside, he wanted to buy, in rapid succession, a cancan doll, a box of cigars, a gardenia corsage, a stuffed toy poodle, a balloon, and a

Europe without George

photograph of the six of us at the table with our arms around each other. Mrs. Cleverhausen wouldn't let him buy anything except the balloon.

We drank some champagne and pretty soon the lights dimmed, the spotlight came on, and the curtains parted to reveal a lavish reproduction of the Gare de Lyon. A lot of young men dressed as porters were wheeling baggage carts around and singing—

> Regardez le chemin-de-fer
> Pouf-pouf! Choo-choo!

And sure enough, with an ear-piercing whistle the chemin-de-fer pulled on stage and half a dozen girls without any clothes on got off it. The girls were carrying little suitcases which they handed to the porters, and then everybody began to dance around and sing some more.

> Regardez le chemin-de-fer
> Pouf-pouf! Choo-choo!

"Whee!" Ferdie shouted, banging on the table with his fork. "Choo-choo! Choo-choo-choo-choo-choo!"

"There's something floating in your champagne," Mrs. Cleverhausen said to me. "Ugh."

I looked down and saw that one of my eyelashes had dropped off and was drifting around my glass, looking for all the world like a little outrigger canoe.

"It seems to be some sort of a centipede," Mrs. Cleverhausen said interestedly. "I'd call the waiter if I were you."

"No, no," I said. "No need to bother the waiter. I'll take care of it."

I fished it out and opened my pocketbook. Just in time, I saw the look on Mrs. Cleverhausen's face. I closed my pocketbook.

"I thought for a minute you were going to put that bug into your pocketbook," she said.

We both laughed gaily.

"Why don't you just throw it on the floor?" Mrs. Cleverhausen said.

I dropped the eyelash to the floor and Mrs. Cleverhausen obligingly squooshed it with her shoe.

"There!" she said. "Nasty thing." She peered down into the gloom under the table. "It must have had fifty legs if it had one," she said. "Some sort of French insect, I imagine."

I turned my attention to the floor show again. The plot must have taken a sharp twist while Mrs. Cleverhausen and I were busy killing my eyelash, because now the scene had shifted inexplicably to a tropical island and the girls were costumed as birds perched around in cocoanut trees. By "costumed" I mean they were wearing bunches of tail-feathers presumably attached to them by Invisible Scotch Brand Mending Tape.

"Those look like pheasant feathers," Mrs. Webberman said in tones of great disapproval. "Barbaric!"

"Pheasant feathers," Ferdie said happily. "French phreasant feathers. Phreasant futhers."

He began to chortle to himself.

"What part of America are you from?" Mrs. Cleverhausen asked me.

"Connecticut," I said.

"Is that anywhere near Chicago?" she asked.

"Not very," I said.

"There was a program about Chicago on the telly last year," she said. "Beautiful city. All those palm trees."

The music was getting louder. Someone had dragged a huge tom-tom on stage and one of the bird-girls was stomping around on top of it.

"This program was all about how you raise your citrus crops in Chicago," Mrs. Cleverhausen said. "Frightfully interesting. And the way the alligators swim right—"

"Fruthers!" Ferdie shouted suddenly. "Phreasant futhers!"

Heads began to turn.

"Time to go," the guide said, hastily standing up. "Allons, monsieurs et mesdames!"

"Allons yourself," Ferdie said. "I came all the way from Australia to see them dance the cancan and I'm not leaving until I do."

The orchestra and the tom-tom were reaching a wild crescendo. The girls had all climbed down from the cocoanut trees now and were doing a sort of snake-dance around the stage.

"All the way from Australia," Ferdie said tearfully, and he began to sing *Waltzing Mathilda* very loudly and off-key.

The guide sat down resignedly.

"How about some more champagne?" Mr. Webberman said.

Mrs. Webberman and Mrs. Cleverhausen said they didn't want any more champagne.

"*I'll* have some more champagne," Ferdie said, abandoning *Waltzing Mathilda* in the middle of a verse. He stood up and his chair fell over with a crash. "Champagne for everybody!" he said. "I'll treat the whole place to champagne."

Between them, Mr. Webberman and the guide managed to pull him down.

"Regardez les Américains," someone at the next table said disapprovingly.

"Hey, who you calling an American?" Ferdie demanded loudly, standing up again. "I'm from Australia and I'm bloody proud of it too."

"Hear, hear," Mr. Webberman said. "You tell 'em, Ferdie, old boy."

The orchestra was so loud now that both Ferdie and Mr. Webberman were shouting over the noise of the music.

"Australia's the greatest li'l country on the face of the earth," Ferdie told the patrons of the Moulin Rouge. "I'll lick anybody who says different."

"Now, hold on a minute," Mr. Webberman said. "The United States happens to be the greatest li'l country face of earth and don' you forget it!"

Hardly anyone in the place was watching the stage any more.

"Australia!" Ferdie shouted, and began to take off his coat and roll up his sleeves.

"United States!" Mr. Webberman told him. "God bless America. Stars 'n stripes forever."

Ferdie took a feeble swing at Mr. Webberman, but missed. I saw two waiters hurrying towards our table, and the whole orchestra was beginning to turn around to see what the commotion was about. I took my pocketbook, got up as surreptitiously as I could, and tiptoed toward the exit.

Just before I closed the door to the lobby behind me, I heard Ferdie start to sing *Waltzing Mathilda* again.

"How was Paris by night?" Chris asked me.

"Pulsating," I said. "Also throbbing."

"What was the cancan like?" she said.

"I didn't stay to see it," I said. "Did you have a nice evening?"

"Fabulous," Chris said. "Alexis is going to save up all his money and come to America to visit me."

"That's nice," I said.

"Of course I'm mad about Alexis," Chris said, "but the funny thing is I'm getting sort of anxious to see Moose again. I think I'm about ready to go home now."

"Me too," I said. "Home to Highmeadow."

"Home to Moose," Chris said, with a deep sigh, "and to Harry and Evelyn and Wilma Vogelsang and Charley MacAllaster and Mrs. Caudlemaier and the good old U.S.A."

"It's the greatest little country on the face of the earth," I said. "I'll lick anyone who says different."

CHAPTER *10*

We were home again.

We were back from Europe with our Braemar sweaters and our blue sunglasses and our Italian sandals and our gondolier's hats. We had an ashtray from Harry's American Bar and a *Do Not Disturb* sign from the Hotel Continentale in Rome. ("If you're sure that's what *Non Disturbate* means," Chris said doubtfully. "It certainly looks strange.")

We had twenty-five rolls of exposed Kodak Instamatic Film, including some breathtaking shots of the Parthenon, the Webbermans, the Arc de Triomphe, Mount Pilatus, the ruins of Pompeii, and Mr. Schreiner.

We had seventeen ball-point pens, one more ball-point pen than we had when we left the United States.

We had presents for all our friends—woolen mufflers from Scotland and Johnny Walker Black Label whisky and hand-embroidered Greek shoulder-bags and Florentine leather wallets and a pair of genuine Minoan cufflinks.

"What did you get for Harry?" Chris asked me.

"Oh, God," I said.

"Never mind," she said. "You can always give him the extra ball-point pen."

"Hey!" Moose said. Chris had her hair piled on top of her head and she was wearing the dead-white lipstick and the raffia sweater and the tight pink silk pants and the Arpège that Alexis had given her as a goodbye present in Paris. "Geez!"

"Hello, Moose," I said.

"H'lo, Mrs. Kampen," Moose said. "Hey, Chris, where'd you get that perfume you're wearing? Wow!"

"Somebody gave it to me in Paris," Chris said. "Listen, Moose, I have the most absolutely devastating thing to tell you. I mean, it's so awful I don't know how to begin."

"That's a cool sweater," Moose said. "I never saw a sweater like that before."

"Listen, Moose," Chris said. "Remember your fraternity pin . . .?"

"It was the fiercest school board election in the history of Highmeadow," Wilma Vogelsang told me. "We came *that* close to getting Dr. Prangweiler on the board. But never mind, there's the special referendum coming up Wednesday and then we'll show them a thing or two."

"What referendum?" I said. "Who's Dr. Prangweiler?"

"Who's Dr. *Prang*weiler?" Wilma said incredulously.

Europe without George

"Are you serious?"

"Wilma," I said, "I don't know what you're talking about."

"You don't?" Wilma said. "Oh, darling, have you been away?"

"Well, how was Europe?" Charley MacAllaster asked, handing me a dry Martini. "Did you like Dubrovnik?"

"Charley—" I said.

"Just about the greatest spot on God's green earth, isn't it?" Charley said.

I took a sip of the Martini.

"We loved it," I said.

"I knew you would," Charley said. "As I remember you were a little reluctant to go, but now aren't you glad you took my advice?"

"I certainly am, Charley," I said.

"I mean, what's the point of going all the way to Europe unless you see Dubrovnik?" Charley said.

The afternoon sun was sinking in a blaze of orange and red over Highmeadow Mountain on the far side of Caudatowa Lake. Outside the picture window in Charley's living room a green velvet lawn sloped down to the fieldstone barbecue pit next to Charley's grape arbor.

"The scenery," Charley said. "The lakes. The mountains. The simple, friendly Jugoslavian peasants. The—well, what's the use of talking? I mean, when you get all through, what can you say?"

I took another sip of the Martini.

"Nothing, Charley," I said. "Absolutely nothing."

He beamed at me happily. Somewhere inside the grape

arbor a Connecticut bird began to sing beneath the Connecticut sky. High overhead a silver jet streaked toward the horizon, bound for Paris or London or Rome or Athens—or, possibly, for Dubrovnik.